THIRD EDI

Study Guide

Frank J. Mandery
Community College of Finger Lakes

Elementary Algebra for College Students

Allen R. Angel
Monroe Community College

PRENTICE HALL
Englewood Cliffs, New Jersey 07632

Editorial production/supervision: *Mariann Murphy*
Pre-press buyer: *Paula Massanaro*
Manufacturing buyer: *Lori Bulwin*
Supplement Acquisitions Editor: *Susan Black*
Acquisitions Editor: *Priscilla McGeehon*

©1992 by Prentice-Hall, Inc.
A Simon & Schuster Company
Englewood Cliffs, New Jersey 07632

Printed in the United States of America

10 9 8 7 6 5 4 3 2

ISBN 0-13-259755-1

Prentice-Hall International (UK) Limited, *London*
Prentice-Hall of Australia Pty. Limited, *Sydney*
Prentice-Hall Canada Inc. *Toronto*
Prentice-Hall Hispanoamericana, S.A., *Mexico*
Prentice-Hall of India Private Limited, *New Delhi*
Prentice-Hall of Japan, Inc., *Tokyo*
Simon & Schuster Asia Pte. Ltd., *Singapore*
Editora Prentice-Hall do Brasil, Ltda., *Rio de Janeiro*

Contents

Chapter 1   Real Numbers

Section 1.1 Study Skills for Success in Mathematics

To the Student

Unlike other subjects, English, History, and Psychology, Mathematics should be studied by doing pencil and paper work rather than just reading the text.

Before you attempt any assignment, I suggest that you first review the explanations in your text for the given assignments, and also review your class notes on that particular topic. When the assignment has been completed, check to see if your answers are correct. If you continuously get a set of questions wrong, go back to the explanations in your text, and review the material again. If you still cannot successfully do the work, then see your instructor for help. If your instructor cannot help you then possibly he could suggest another source. At times a question will have many different solutions which are not always included in the set of answers. If that's the case, each solution is equally correct.

Remember, success in mathematics depends on understanding. One way to achieve understanding is by successfully completing each assignment on time. Participation and involvement in your class are also key ingredients to success.

Some helpful tips for success:

1) Always attend class. If you are going to be absent, try and get the missing material from a classmate.

2) Take notes in class. Your instructor will cover topics he or she considers important, and will most likely put on a test.

3) Read your text. Become familiar with all the student learning features of your text. Does your text have example problems, practice tests, and answers for the exercises?

4) Always do your assignment as soon as possible after your class, and then review before your next class.

5) If you need help, try and obtain it right away rather than wait several classes.

6) Do not become passive. Get involved and participate.

Section 1.2 — Fractions

Summary:

> **Multiplication Symbols**
> If **a** and **b** stand for (or represent) any two mathematical quantities then each of the following may be used to indicate the product of **a** and **b** ("**a** times **b**").
>
> $$ab, \ a \cdot b, \ a(b), \ (a)b, \ (a)(b)$$
>
> If **a** $\cdot$ **b** = **c** then **a** and **b** are factors of **c**.
>
> **To reduce a fraction to its lowest terms**
> 1. Find the largest number that will divide (without remainder) into both the numerator and the denominator. This number is called the **greatest common factor** (GCF).
>
> 2. Divide both the numerator and the demoninator by the greatest common factor.

Example 1   For each fraction find the greatest common factor (GCF) and reduce to lowest terms.

a) $^{14}/_{21}$ Solution: GCF is 7

$$^{14}/_{21} \ = \ ^{(14 \div 7)}/_{(21 \div 7)} \ = \ ^{2}/_{3}$$

b) $^{30}/_{50}$ Solution: GCF is (?)

$$^{30}/_{50} \ = \ ^{(30 \div (?))}/_{(50 \div (?))} = \ ^{3}/_{5}$$

c) $^{108}/_{144}$ Solution: GCF is (?)

$$^{108}/_{144} = \ ^{(108 \div (?))}/_{(144 \ (?))} = \ ^{(?)}/_{(?)}$$

Answers for (?) in Example 1b) GCF is 10; $^{3}/_{5}$
                                   1c) GCF is 36; $^{3}/_{4}$

Summary:

> **Multiplication of Fractions**
> $^{a}/_{b} \cdot \ ^{c}/_{d} = \ ^{ac}/_{bd}$

Example 2

a) Multiply $^5/_{12} \cdot {}^3/_{10}$

Solution: $\quad {}^5/_{12} \cdot {}^3/_{10} \quad = \quad {}^{(5 \cdot 3)}/_{(12 \cdot 10)} \quad = {}^{15}/_{120}$ *GCF is 15*

$\quad\quad\quad {}^{15}/_{120} \quad\quad = \quad {}^{(15 \div 15)}/_{(120 \div 15)} = {}^1/_8$ *Answer*

b) Multiply $^{18}/_5 \cdot {}^{20}/_9$

Solution: $\quad {}^{18}/_5 \cdot {}^{20}/_9 = {}^{(18 \cdot 20)}/_{(5 \cdot 9)} = {}^{(?)}/_{(?)}$ *GCF is 45*

$\quad\quad\quad {}^{(?)}/_{(?)} = {}^{[(?) \div 45]}/_{[(?) \div 45]} = {}^8/_1$ *Answer*

c) Multiply $^{120}/_{45} \cdot {}^{90}/_{100}$

Solution: ${}^{120}/_{45} \cdot {}^{90}/_{100} = \overset{6}{\cancel{120}}/\underset{1}{45} \cdot \overset{2}{\cancel{90}}/\underset{5}{100} = {}^{(6 \cdot 2)}/_{(1 \cdot 5)} = {}^{(?)}/_{(?)}$ *Answer*

d) Multiply $^9/_{10} \cdot {}^{20}/_3$

Solution: $\quad {}^9/_{10} \cdot {}^{20}/_3 = {}^9/_{10} \cdot \overset{3}{\cancel{20}}/\underset{1}{\cancel{3}}$ (Divided by ?)

$\quad\quad = {}^3/\underset{1}{\cancel{10}} \cdot \overset{2}{\cancel{20}}/_1$ (Divided by ?)

$\quad\quad = {}^3/_1 \cdot {}^2/_1 = {}^6/_1 = 6$ *Answer*

Answers for (?) in Example 2.

b) $^{360}/_{45}$; c) $^{12}/_5$; d) Divided by 3
Divided by 10

Summary:

Division of Fractions
$^a/_b \div {}^c/_d = {}^a/_b \cdot {}^d/_c = {}^{ad}/_{bc}$

Example 3

a) Evaluate $^8/_9 \div {}^{12}/_{18}$

Solution: $\quad {}^8/_9 \div {}^{12}/_{18} = {}^8/_9 \cdot {}^{18}/_{12} = {}^{(8 \cdot 18)}/_{9 \cdot 12} = {}^{144}/_{108}$ *GCF is 36*

$\quad\quad = {}^{(144 \div 36)}/_{(108 \div 36)} = {}^4/_3$ *Answer*

b) Evaluate $^5/_9 \div {}^{10}/_3$

Solution: $\quad {}^5/_9 \div {}^{10}/_3 = {}^5/_9 \cdot {}^3/_{10} = \overset{1}{\cancel{5}}/_9 \cdot {}^3/\underset{2}{\cancel{10}}$ (Divided by ?)

$\quad\quad = {}^1/_9 \cdot \overset{}{\cancel{3}}/\underset{3}{}2$ (Divided by ?)

$\quad\quad = {}^1/_3 \cdot {}^1/_2 = {}^1/_6$ *Answer*

c) Evaluate $\quad {}^3/_{100} \div {}^{18}/_{10}$

Solution: $\quad {}^3/_{100} \div {}^{18}/_{10} = {}^3/_{100} \cdot {}^{10}/_{18}$

$$= {}^3/_{100} \cdot {}^{10}/_{\cancel{18}}^{\,1} \qquad \text{(Divided by ?)}$$

$$= {}^1/_{\cancel{100}}^{\,1}_{\,10} \cdot {}^{\cancel{10}}/_{6}^{\,6} \qquad \text{(Divided by ?)}$$

$$= {}^1/_{10} \cdot {}^1/_6 = {}^{(?)}/_{(?)} \qquad \textbf{\textit{Answer}}$$

Answers for (?) in Example 3.

b) Divided by 5 ; Divided by 3

c) Divided by 3 ; Divided by 10 ; ${}^1/_{60}$

> ## Addition and Subtraction of Fractions
>
> $${}^a/_c + {}^b/_c = {}^{a+b}/_c \quad \text{or} \quad {}^a/_c - {}^b/_c = {}^{a-b}/_c$$

Example 4

a) Evaluate $\quad {}^{11}/_{24} + {}^4/_{24}$

Solution: $\quad {}^{11}/_{24} + {}^4/_{24} = {}^{(11+4)}/_{24} = {}^{15}/_{24} \qquad \textbf{\textit{(GCF is ?)}}$

$$= {}^{15}/_{24} = {}^{(15 \div ?)}/_{(24 \div ?)} = {}^5/_8 \qquad \textbf{\textit{Answer}}$$

b) Evaluate $\quad {}^5/_{16} + {}^3/_5$

Solution: $\quad {}^5/_{16} = {}^5/_{16} \cdot {}^5/_5 = {}^{(?)}/_{80}$

$$ {}^3/_5 = {}^3/_5 \cdot {}^{16}/_{16} = {}^{(?)}/_{80}$$

$$ {}^5/_{16} + {}^3/_5 = {}^{25}/_{80} + {}^{48}/_{80} = {}^{(25+48)}/_{80} = {}^{(?)}/_{80}$$

c) Evaluate $\quad {}^3/_5 - {}^1/_3$

Solution: $\quad {}^3/_5 = {}^{(?)}/_{15}$

$$ {}^1/_3 = {}^{(?)}/_{15}$$

$$ {}^3/_5 - {}^1/_3 = {}^9/_{15} - {}^5/_{15} = {}^{(9-5)}/_{15} = {}^{(?)}/_{15}$$

Answers for (?) in Example 4
    a) GCF is 3
    b) 25 ; 48 ; 73
    c) 9; 5; 4

> ## To Change a Mixed Number to a Fraction
>
> 1) Multiply the denominator of the fraction in the mixed number by the whole number preceding it.
>
> 2) Add the numerator of the fraction in the mixed number to the product obtained in step 1. This sum represents the numerator of the fraction we are seeking. The denominator of the fraction we are seeking is the same as the denominator of the fraction in the mixed number.

Example 5

a) Change the mixed number $3\,^4/_5$ to a fraction
   Solution: $3\,^4/_5 = {}^{(15+4)}/_5 = {}^{19}/_5$

Multiply the denominator, 5, by the whole number,3, to get a product of 15. To this product add the numerator, 4. This sum, 19, represents the numerator of the fraction. The denominator of the fraction in the mixed number, 5.

b) Change the mixed number $17\,^9/_{12}$ a fraction
   Solution: $17\,^9/_{12} = {}^{(204+9)}/_{12} = {}^{213}/_{12}$

To Change a Fraction Greater Than 1 to a Mixed Number

1) Divide the numerator by the denominator. Note the quotient, remainder, and divisor.

2) Write the mixed number. The quotient found in step 1 is the whole number part of the mixed number. The remainder is the numerator of the fraction in the mixed number, and the divisor is the denominator of the fraction in the mixed number. The denominator in the fraction of the mixed number will be the same as the denominator in the answer.

Example 6 Convert $^{103}/_3$ to a mixed number

Solution: $3\,^{34}/_{103}$ $^{103}/_3 = 34\,^1/_3$

Example 7 Add $5\,^9/_{16}$ to $^7/_8$
Change $^7/_8$ to $^{14}/_{16}$
$5\,^9/_{16} + {}^7/_8 = {}^{89}/_{16} + {}^{14}/_{16}$
$= {}^{(89+14)}/_{16}$
$= {}^{103}/_{16}$ **or** $6\,^7/_{16}$

Example 8 Multiply $(9\,^2/_5)(8\,^7/_8)$

Solution: Change both mixed numbers to fractions; then multiply.
Rename $9\,^2/_5$ to $^{47}/_5$
Rename $8\,^7/_9$ to $^{79}/_9$

$(9\,^2/_5)(8\,^7/_8) = {}^{47}/_5 \cdot {}^{79}/_9 = {}^{3713}/_{45}$ **or** $82\,^{23}/_{45}$

Example 9   Divide $^9/_{16} \div 9\,^4/_5$

Solution: Rename $9\,^4/_5$ to $^{49}/_5$

$$^9/_{16} \div 9\,^4/_5 = \,^9/_{16} \div \,^{49}/_5$$
$$= \,^9/_{16} \cdot \,^5/_{49}$$
$$= \,^{45}/_{784}$$

Exercise Set l.2

Reduce each fraction to its lowest terms. If a fraction is presently in its lowest terms, so state.

1) $^2/_6$ 2) $^6/_{10}$ 3) $^{18}/_{45}$ 4) $^7/_{15}$ 5) $^{40}/_{52}$

Find the product or quotients, and write in lowest terms.

6) $^2/_3 \cdot \,^6/_7$ 7) $^6/_8 \cdot \,^4/_9$ 8) $^{10}/_{18} \cdot \,^9/_5$ 9) $^{35}/_{72} \cdot \,^{18}/_{56}$
10) $^7/_{12} \div \,^1/_3$ 11) $^3/_{16} \div \,^9/_{20}$ 12) $4 \div \,^2/_5$ 13) $^4/_9 \div 36$
14) $7\,^1/_2 \cdot \,^4/_5$ 15) $^{32}/_{70} \cdot 4\,^3/_8$ 16) $^5/_8 \div 3\,^3/_4$ 17) $10\,^2/_9 \div \,^2/_{81}$

Add or subtract. Write answers in lowest terms.

18) $^7/_{15} + \,^8/_{15}$ 19) $^{70}/_{81} - \,^{19}/_{81}$ 20) $^2/_6 + \,^1/_8$ 21) $^7/_{10} - \,^3/_5$
22) $^3/_4 + \,^2/_{14}$ 23) $^{12}/_{30} - \,^1/_5$ 24) $^6/_7 + \,^4/_{12}$ 25) $7\,^2/_8 + \,^3/_8$
26) $4\,^1/_2 - \,^5/_6$ 27) $^3/_5 + 7\,^1/_5$ 28) $3\,^5/_8 - 2\,^1/_4$

29) When a $1^1/_8$ pound pork roast was trimmed of fat, it weighed $^3/_4$ pound. How much fat was removed?

30) Mr. Pellerito built a bookshelf 42 inches long. How many books that are $^3/_4$ inches thick can be stood on that shelf?

31) This past summer Kurt Mandery drove across the country in three days. On Monday he drove $4\,^1/_2$ hours, on Tuesday $12\,^3/_4$ hours, on Wednesday $8\,^1/_3$ hours. What was the total driving time for the trip?

32) It cost each $15\,^3/_4$ to enter Darien Lake Amusement Park for the day. How much would it cost a family of four to enter the park?

Answers for Exercise Set 1.2

1) $^1/_3$ 2) $^3/_5$ 3) $^2/_5$ 4) lowest terms   5) $^{10}/_{13}$
6) $^4/_7$ 7) $^1/_3$ 8) 1   9) $^5/_{32}$ 10) $^7/_4$
11) $^5/_{12}$ 12) 10   13) $^1/_{81}$ 14) 6   15) 8
16) $^1/_6$ 17) 414   18) 1   19) $^{17}/_{27}$ 20) $^{11}/_{24}$
21) $^1/_{10}$ 22) $^{25}/_{28}$ 23) $^1/_5$ 24) $^{25}/_{21}$ 25) $7\,^5/_8$

26) $3^2/_3$ 27) $7^4/_5$ 28) $1^3/_8$ 29) $^3/_8$ 30) 56
31) $25\,^7/_{12}$ 32) $63.00

Section 1.3 The Real Number System

Summary:

Real
Numbers
Natural Numbers {1, 2, 3, 4, 5, …}
Whole Numbers {0, 1, 2, 3, 4, 5,…}
Integers {…,-5, -4, -3, -2, -1, 0, 1, 2, 3, 4, 5, …}
Rational Numbers {quotient of two integers, denominator not 0}
Irrational Numbers   Examples $\sqrt{2}$, $\sqrt{5}$, π

**Real Number {All numbers that can be represented
on the real number line.}**

Example 1   Consider the following set of numbers:
{-0.3 , π , -6 , $-^1/_2$, 1.75 , $3^1/_4$, 0 , $\sqrt{2}$, 5 , -0.25}

List the elements of the set that are:
a) Natural Numbers   b) Whole Numbers
c) Integers   d) Rational Numbers
e) Irrational Numbers   f) Real Numbers

Solution:
a) 5   b) 0, 5
c) -6, 0, 5   d) -0.3, -6, $-^1/_2$, 1.75, $3^1/_4$, 0, 5, -0.25
e) π, $\sqrt{2}$ f) -0.3, π, -6, $-^1/_2$, 1.75, $3^1/_4$, 0, $\sqrt{2}$, 5, -0.25

Exercise Set 1.3

List the elements of each of the following sets, if possible.
1) Natural Numbers between 5 and 11.
2) The first 3 Whole Numbers.
3) Integers between -5 and 2.
4) Natural Numbers less than 1.
5) Even Natural Numbers.

State whether the following statements are True or False.
6) $^1/_2$ is a member of the set of Integers.
7) 0 is a member of the Natural Numbers.
8) The set of all Integers are members of the set of Rational Numbers.
9) $\sqrt{2}$ is a member of the set of Irrational Numbers.
10) The set of Real Numbers contains the Natural Numbers, Whole Numbers, Integers, Rational Numbers, and Irrational Numbers.

Answers for Exercise Set 1.3

1) {6, 7, 8, 9, 10}
2) {0, 1, 2}
3) {-4, -3, -2, -1, 0, 1}
4) No Answer
5) {2, 4, 6, 8, 10,...}
6) False
7) False
8) True
9) True
10) True

Section 1.4 Inequalities

Summary:

> The number line can be used to explain inequalities. When comparing two numbers, **the number farther to the right on the number line is the greater number, and the number farther to the left is the lesser number.** The symbol > is used to represent the words "greater than". The symbol < is used to represent the words "less than".
>
> **The student should remember that the point of the inequality symbol will always point to the lesser number.**

Example 1   Insert either > or < in the space between the paired numbers to make the statement correct.

a) -3   -1   b) $^3/_4$ 0
c) 2 $^1/_2$ 5   d) -3.75   3.75

Solution:

a) -3 < -1, since -3 is to the left of -1.
b) $^3/_4$ > O since $^3/_4$ is to the right of 0.
c) $2^1/_2$ < 5, since $2^1/_2$ is to the (?) of 5.
d) -3.75 < 3.75, since -3.75 is to the (?) of 3.75.

Answers to (?) in Example 1   c) left   d) left

Summary:

> The absolute value of a number can be considered the distance between the number and zero on the number line. The absolute value of every number will be either positive or zero.

Example 2   Insert either > , < , or = to make the statement true.

a) $|3| = 3$ b) $|^3/_4| = ^3/_4$

c) $|2.75| > -2.75$ d) $-5 < |5|$

Solution:

a) $|-3| = 3$, since $|-3| = 3$

b) $|^3/_4| = ^3/_4$, since $|^3/_4| = ^3/_4$

c) $|2.75| > -2.75$, since $|2.75| = 2.75$ and 2.75 is to the rIght of -2.75.

d) $-5 < |5|$, since $|5| = 5$ and -5 is to the left of 5.

Exercise Set 1.4

Insert either < or > to make each expression true.

1) $^1/_2 < 3$ 2) $-1 > -2$

3) $5 > -5$ 4) $0 < 3^1/_2$

5) $-1 < -^1/_2$ 6) $-3.5 < 3.5$

7) $\sqrt{2} > -\sqrt{2}$ 8) $0.25 > -0.25$

9) $1.25 < 1.75$ 10) $-7 < -1$

Insert either < , > , or = to make each statement true.

11) $|14|$ 6   12) $|-3|$ $|4|$

13) $|-0.5|$ $|0.5|$ 14) $|3.1|$ 5.5

15) $|-0.0019|$ 0.0019   16) 1^3 4 $|-2^7/_{16}|$

17) $|457|$ -457   18) -19 $|-19|$

19) 23 $|-27|$ 20) $|-21|$ $|-18|$

Answers for Exercise Set 1.4

1)	$^1/_2$	<	3	2)	-1	>	-2
3)	5	>	-5	4)	0	<	$3^1/_2$
5)	-1	<	$-^1/_2$	6)	-3.5	<	3.5
7)	$\sqrt{2}$	>	$-\sqrt{2}$	8)	0.25	>	-0.25
9)	1.25	<	1.75	10)	-7	<	-1
11)	$|14|$	>	6	12)	$|-3|$	<	$|4|$
13)	$|-0.5|$	=	$|0.5|$	14)	$|3.1|$	<	5.5
15)	$|-0.0019|$	=	0.0019	16)	$1^3/_4$	<	$|-2^7/_{16}|$
17)	$|457|$	>	-457	18)	-19	<	$|-19|$
19)	23	<	$|-27|$	20)	$|-21|$	>	$|-18|$

Section 1.5 Addition of Real Numbers

Summary:

> Any two numbers whose sum is zero are said to be **opposites (or additive inverses)** of each other. In general, if we let a represent any real number, then its opposite is -a and a + (-a) = 0.

Example 1   Find the opposite of each number.
            a) -14.2   b) 17

Solution:

a) The opposite of -14.2 is 14.2, since 14.2 + (-14.2) = 0.
b) The opposite of 17 is -17, since 17 + (-17) = 0.

Summary:

> **To add real numbers with the same sign** (either both positive or both negative), add their absolute values. The sum has the same sign as the numbers being added.

Example 2   **a.)** Add 14 + 6 $= 20$

Solution: Since both numbers have the same sign, both positive, we add their absolute values:
                $|14| + |6| = 14 + 6 = 20$

                Since both numbers being added are positive, the sum is positive. Thus 14 + 6 = 20.

                b) An airplane cruising at an altitude of 12,460 ft. is ordered by a tower controller to climb 440 ft. What will the plane's new altitude be?

Solution: Since increase in altitude would represent positive value simply add 12,460 + 440. $= 12,900$

                12,460 + 440 = 12,900 feet

Example 3   a) Add -7 + (-9) $= -16$

Solution: Since both numbers have the same sign, both negative, we add their absolute values: $|-7| + |-9| = 7 + 9 = 16$. Since both numbers being added are negative their sum is negative. Thus -7 + (-9) = -16.

                b) At 2 a.m. the temperature in Cut Bank, Montana, was -15° F. If the temperature dropped another 15° F by 6 a.m., what was the temperature at that time?

Solution: Since a decrease in temperature would represent negative value, simply add -15° + (-15°). Thus -15° + (-15) = -30° F.

➡NOTE: **The sum of two positive numbers will always be positive and the sum of two negative numbers will always be negative.**

Summary:

> **To add two signed numbers with different signs** (one positive and the other negative), find the difference between the larger absolute value and the smaller absolute value. The answer has the sign of the number with the larger absolute value.

Example 4   a) Add   -8 + 3 = -5
                  b) Add   9 + (-4) = 5
                  c) Add   6 + (-17) = -11

Solution: Since the two numbers being added have different signs, find the difference between the larger absolute value and the smaller.

a) $-8 + 3 = |-8| - |3| = 8 - 3 = 5$, since $|-8|$ is greater than $|3|$, the sum is negative.
            Thus $-8 + 3 = -5$.

b) $9 + (-4) = |9| - |-4| = 9 - 4 = 5$, since $|9|$ is greater than $|-4|$, the sum is positive.
            Thus $9 + (-4) = 5$.

c) $6 + (-17) = |-17| - |6| = 17 - 6 = 11$, since $|-17|$ is greater than $|6|$, the sum is negative.
            Thus $6 + (-17) = -11$.

➡NOTE: **The sum of two signed numbers with different signs may be either positive or negative. The sign of the sum will be the sign of the number with the larger absolute value.**

Exercise Set 1.5

State the opposite of each number.
        1) -25   2) 3.14   3) $-\frac{71}{256}$ 4) $-\sqrt{17}$

Add as indicated:

5) 8 + (-5)	6) -27 + (-13)	7) 218 + (-113)
8) -6 + (-8)	9) -15 + 18	10) -36 + 54
11) -0.3 + 0.3	12) -2.4 + (-1.6)	13) -2.4 + 1.6
14) $^7/_8$ + (-$^3/_8$)	15) -$^3/_4$ + (-$^3/_4$)	16) -80 + 121
17) 13 + 18	18) -0.3 + (-0.9)	

19) Michelle Mandery has a balance of $ - 473.29 on her Visa card account. She made a payment of $238.43. Find her new balance.

20) A scuba diver descends to a depth of 141 feet below sea level. His buddy dives 49 feet deeper. What is his buddy's altitude at the deepest point of his dive?

Answers for Exercise Set 1.5

1) 25	2) -3.14	3) $^{71}/_{256}$	4) $\sqrt{17}$
5) 3	6) -40	7) 105	8) -14
9) 3	10) 18	11) 0	12) -4.0
13) -0.8	14) $^4/_8$, $^1/_2$	15) -$^6/_4$, -$^3/_2$	16) 41
17) 31	18) -1.2	19) $ -234.86	20) -190 ft.

Section 1.6 — Subtraction of Real Numbers

Summary:

> **Subtraction of Real Numbers**
> In general, if a and b represent any two real numbers, then
> **a - b = a + (-b)**

Example 1

a) Evaluate   2 - 6
Solution:

Subtraction Problem		Addition Problem		Answer
2 - 6	=	2 + (-6)	=	-4

subtract positive 6   *add* negative 6

b) Evaluate   -19 - 20
Solution:

Subtraction Problem		Addition Problem		Answer
-19 - 20	=	-19 + (-20)	=	(?)

subtract positive 20   *add* negative 20

c) Evaluate   25 - (-12)
Solution: 25 - (-12) = 25 + (?) = (?)

d) Evaluate   -3 - 8
Solution: -3 - 8 = -3 (?) 8 = (?)

e) Linda Mandery has a balance of $473.29 in her checking account. Find her new balance after she writes a check for $510.29.

Solution: $473.29 - $510.29 = $473.29 + (?) = $-37.00
                   The negative indicates a deficit of $37.

Answers Example 1:

b) -39   c) 12 , 37
d) +, 5   e) $-510.29

Exercise Set 1.6

Evaluate each expression:
1) 4 - 9   2) 5 - (-3)   3) -3 - 4
4) -8 - 1   5) -2 - (-7)   6) 9 - 9
7) 4 - (-6)   8) -5 - 5   9) 7 - 8
10) 9 - (-6)   11) -8 - 6   12) 4 - (-5)
13) -0.8 - 1.5   14) 1.8 - 2.3   15) -2.6 - (3.8)
16) 18 - 23 + (-5)   17) 35 -11 - 20   18) -45 + 6 - 30
19) Subtract -5 from 3   20) Subtract -89 from 284.
21) Subtract $^5/_{16}$ from $^2/_{16}$.   22) Subtract - $^3/_8$ from $^2/_8$.

23) At 4 a.m. the temperature at Stanley, North Dakota, was -5.6° F. At 1 p.m. the temperature was 40.6° F. What was the increase in temperature?

24) Mike Pellerito, a scuba driver descends to a depth of 141 feet below sea level. Dan, his brother, dives to a depth of 199 feet below sea level. How much further did Dan dive?

Answers for Exercise Set 1.6

1) -5	2) 8	3) -7	4) -9	5) 5	6) 0
7) 10	8) -10	9) -1	10) 15	11) -14	12) 9
13) -2.3	14) -0.5	15) -6.4	16) -10	17) 4	18) -69
19) 8	20) 373	21) - $^3/_{16}$	22) $^5/_8$	23) 46.2° F	24) 58 ft.

Section 1.7 Multiplication and Division of Real Numbers

Summary:

> **Multiplication of Real Numbers**
> 1) The product of two numbers with like signs is **a positive number.**
> 2) The product of two numbers with unlike signs is **a negative number.**

Example 1

a)   Evaluate   5(-2)
     Solution: 5(-2) = -10   Rule 2 from above.

b)   Evaluate   (-2)(-4)
     Solution: (-2)(-4) = ?8   Rule 1 from above.

c)   Evaluate   -6 • 5
     Solution: -6 • 5 = ?30   Rule 2 from above.

d)   Evaluate   (-92)0
     Solution: (-92)0 = ?

Answers Example 1

b) positive 8   c) negative 30   d) O

Summary:

> The product of an even number of negative numbers will always be **positive.**
> The product of an odd number of negative numbers will always be **negative.**

Example 2

a)   Evaluate   (-1)(-2)(-2)(-3)
     Solution: (-1)(-2)(-2)(-3)   =   2(-2)(-3)
                                          =   (-4)(-3)
                                          =   12

b)   Evaluate   (2)(-3)(-1)(5)
     Solution: (2)(-3)(-1)(5)   =   (-6)(-1)(5)
                                         =   (?)(5)
                                         =   (?)

c)   Evaluate   (-19)(25)(0)(-1)(10)(47)
     Solution: (-19)(25)(0)(-1)(10)(47) =   ?

Answers for (?) in Example 2   b) 6, 30   c) O

➡Note that zero times any real number equals zero.

Summary:

> **Division of Real Numbers**
> 1) The quotient of two numbers with **like signs** is a **positve** number.
> 2) The quotient of two numbers with **unlike signs** is a **negative** number.

Example 3

    a)   Evaluate $^{-108}/_{-6}$

            Solution: $^{-108}/_{-6} = 18$ Rule 1 from above.

    b)   Evaluate $^{-42}/_{7}$

            Solution: $^{-42}/_{7} = (?)6$ Rule 2 from above.

    c)   Evaluate $^{0.56}/_{-0.8}$

            Solution: $^{0.56}/_{-0.8} = ?\ 0.7$ Rule 2 from above.

    d)   Evaluate $^{1}/_{4} \div {^{3}/_{-8}}$

            Solution: $^{1}/_{4} \div {^{3}/_{-8}} = {^{1}/_{4}} \cdot {^{-8}/_{3}} = {^{(?)}/_{(?)}} \div {^{(?)}/_{(?)}}$

Answers for (?) in Example 3.
b) negative   c) negative   d) $^{-8}/_{12}$, $^{-2}/_{3}$

Summary:

> If **a** and **b** represent any real numbers, **b ≠ 0**, then
> $$^{a}/_{-b} = {^{-a}/_{b}} = - {^{a}/_{b}}$$

Example 4

    $^{7}/_{-16} = {^{-7}/_{16}} = - {^{7}/_{16}}$

Summary:

> **For Multiplication and Division**
> (+)(+) = +   *like* signs positive
> (-) (-) = +
>
> (+)(-) = -   *unlike* signs negative
> (-) (+) = -

Summary:

> ### Division Involving Zero
>
> $\frac{0}{a} = 0$, $a \neq 0$; $\frac{a}{0}$ is undefined, $a \neq 0$; $\frac{0}{0}$ is indeterminate

Example 5 $\frac{0}{16} = 0$, $\frac{16}{0}$ = undefined

Exercise Set 1.7

Find the product.

1) 4(-6)	2) (-5) 2	3) (-7)(5)
4) (-8) (-2)	5) (-6)(-7)	6) 8(-4)
7) 9(-5)	8) (-30)(-20)	9) (3.04)(-100)
10) (-0.5)(0.5)	11) $\frac{-7}{8} \cdot \frac{4}{3}$	12) $\frac{-3}{5} \cdot \frac{-1}{6}$

Find the quotient.

13) $\frac{10}{-2}$	14) $\frac{-6}{3}$	15) $\frac{-27}{-9}$
16) $\frac{56}{8}$	17) $\frac{-45}{15}$	18) $\frac{1.25}{-0.25}$
19) (-108) ÷ 2	20) 121 ÷ (-11)	
21) (-740) ÷ (-10)	22) $\frac{5}{2}$ ÷ (-5)	
23) $\frac{17}{5}$ ÷ (-17)	24) $\frac{-6}{3}$ ÷ $\frac{-2}{3}$	

Indicate whether the following is 0, undefined, or indeterminate.

25) $\frac{0}{-19}$ 26) $\frac{\sqrt{3}}{0}$ 27) $\frac{0}{0}$ 28) $\frac{0}{-148}$

Answers for Exercise Set 1.7

1) -24	2) -10	3) -35	4) 16
5) 42	6) -32	7) -45	8) 600
9) -304	10) -0.25	11) $\frac{-7}{6}$	12) $\frac{1}{10}$
13) -5	14) -2	15) 3	16) 7
17) -3	18) -5	19) -54	20) -11
21) 74	22) $-\frac{1}{2}$	23) 1	24) 3
25) 0	26) undefined	27) indeterminate	28) 0

Section 1.8 — An Introduction to Exponents

Summary:

> In general, the number **b** to the **n**th power, written b^n, means
>
> $$b \cdot b \cdot b \cdots \cdots = b^n$$
> n factors of **b**

Example 1

Evaluate each expression

a) 3^3 b) 5^2 c) 10^5

d) $(-1)^5$ e) $(-2)^6$ f) $(2/3)^3$

Solution:

a) $3^3 = 3 \cdot 3 \cdot 3 = 27$

b) $5^2 = (\,?\,)(\,?\,) = (?)$

c) $10^5 = 10 \cdot 10 \cdot 10 \cdot 10 \cdot 10 = (?)$

d) $(-1)^5 = (?)\,(?)\,(?)\,(?)\,(?) = (?)$

e) $(-2)^6 = (?)\,(?)\,(?)\,(?)\,(?)\,(?) = (?)$

f) $(2/3)^3 = 2/3 \cdot 2/3 \cdot 2/3 = (?/?)$

Answers for (?) in Example 1.

b) 5, 5, 25

c) 100,000

d) (-1)(-1)(-1)(-1)(-1), -1

e) (-2)(-2)(-2)(-2)(-2)(-2) , 64

f) $8/27$

Example 2

Write each expression as a product of factors.

a) a^4b b) $12h^2k$ c) 5^3bw^3 d) $3^4m^2y^5$

Solution:

a) $a^4b = a \cdot a \cdot a \cdot a \cdot b$

b) $12h^2k = 12 \cdot (h) \cdot (?) \cdot (?)$

c) $5^3bw^3 = 5 \cdot (?) \cdot (?) \cdot (b) \cdot (w) \cdot (?) \cdot (?)$

d) $3^4m^2y^5 = 3 \cdot 3 \cdot (?) \cdot (?) \cdot (m) \cdot (?) \cdot (y) \cdot (?) \cdot (?) \cdot (?) \cdot (?)$

Answers for (?) in Example 2.

b) h,k   c) 5,5,w, w   d) 3,3,m,y,y,y,y

Note the following difference

$-a^2 = -(a)(a)$

$(-a)^2 = (-a)(-a)$

Example 3

Evaluate each expression.

a) -3^2 b) $(-3)^2$ c) -1^4 d) $(-1)^4$

Solution:

a) $-3^2 = -(3)(3) = -(?) = -9$

b) $(-3)^2 = (-3)(-3) = (?)$

c) $-1^4 = -(1)(1)(?)(?) = -(?) = -1$

d) $(-1)^4 = (-1)(-1)(?)(?) = (?)$

Answers for (?) in Example 3.

a) 9　　　　　b) 9　　　　　c) 1, 1, 1　　　　　d) -1, -1, 1

Exercise Set 1.8

Evaluate each expression.

1) 3^3	2) 2^4	3) $(-5)^2$	4) $(-6)^3$
5) 7^2	6) 3^4	7) 0^3	8) -10^2
9) 5^3	10) -1^8	11) $(-1)8$	12) $(1/2)^2$
13) $(2/3)^3$	14) $(0.2)^3$	15) $(0.4)2$	16) $2^3 \cdot 7$
17) $3^2 \cdot 4^3$	18) $5^2 \cdot (-1)^5$	19) $10^3 \cdot 10^2$	20) $6^2 \cdot 9^2$

Express in exponential form.

21) $w \cdot w \cdot w \cdot y \cdot y$　　　　　22) $3 \cdot 3 \cdot 3 \cdot a \cdot b \cdot b$

23) $7 \cdot m \cdot m$　　　　　24) $6 \cdot b \cdot c \cdot b \cdot c$

Express as a product of factors.

25) $3m^4n^2$　　　26) 16^3wy^2　　　27) -7^3m　　　28) $(-7)^3mp^4$

Evaluate (a) x^3 and (b) $-x^3$, for each of the following values of x.

29) 3　　　　　30) -2

Answers for Exercise Set 1.8

1) 27	2) 16	3) 25	4) -216
5) 49	6) 81	7) 0	8) -100
9) 125	10) -1	11) 1	12) $1/4$
13) $8/27$	14) 0.008	15) 0.16	16) 56
17) 576	18) -25	19) 100,000	20) 2,916
21) w^3y^2	22) 3^3ab^2	23) $7m^2$	24) $6b^2c^2$

25) $3 \cdot m \cdot m \cdot m \cdot m \cdot n \cdot n$　　　　26)　$16 \cdot 16 \cdot 16 \cdot w \cdot y \cdot y$

27) $-(7)(7)(7) \cdot m$　　　　28)　$(-7)(-7)(-7) \cdot m \cdot p \cdot p \cdot p \cdot p$

29) 27, -27　　　　30)　-8, 8

Section 1.9　Use of Parentheses and Priority of Operations

Summary:

1) First, evaluate the information within parentheses, ( ), or brackets, [ ]. If the expression contains nested parentheses (one pair of parentheses within another pair), evaluate the information in the innermost parentheses first.
2) Next, evaluate all exponents.
3) Next, evaluate all multiplications or divisions in the order in which they occur, working from left to right.
4) Finally, evaluate all additions or subtractions in the order in which they occur, working from left to right.

Example 1

a)   Evaluate $7 \cdot 5 + 45$

         Solution: $7 \cdot 5 + 45$

$$= (7 \cdot 5) + 45$$
$$= 35 + 45$$
$$= (?)$$

b)   Evaluate $(10^2)10 + 100$

         Solution: $(10^2)10 + 100$

$$= [(10)(10)]10 + 100$$
$$= (?)\ 10 + 100$$
$$= 1000 + 100$$
$$= (?)$$

c)   Evaluate $10 \cdot 3^2 - 4^2$

         Solution: $10 \cdot 3^2 - 4^2$

$$= 10 \cdot (3)(3) - 4^2$$
$$= 10 \cdot (?) - 4^2$$
$$= 10 \cdot (?) - (4)(4)$$
$$= 10 \cdot 9 - 16$$
$$= 90 - 16$$
$$= (?)$$

d)   Evaluate $48 \div 4 \cdot 2(6) + 15$

         Solution: $48 \div 4 \cdot 2(6) + 15$

$$= (48 \div 4) \cdot 2(6) + 15$$
$$= (?) \cdot 2(6) + 15$$
$$= [12 \cdot 2](6) + 15$$
$$= 24(6) + 15$$
$$= 144 + 15$$
$$= (?)$$

e)   Evaluate $-2 \cdot [20 \div (-2 + 1(-2))] + 6$

         Solution: $-2 \cdot [20 \div (-2 + 1(-2))] + 6$

$$= -2 \cdot [20 \div (-2 + (-2)] + 6$$
$$= -2 \cdot [20 \div (-4)] + 6$$
$$= -2 \cdot (?) + 6$$
$$= (-2 \cdot (-5)) + 6$$
$$= (10) + 6$$
$$= (?)$$

f)   Evaluate $a^2 + 5a$ when $a = 4$

         Solution: $a^2 + 5a = (4)^2 + 5(4)$

$$= [(4)(4)] + 5(4)$$
$$= (?) + 5(4)$$
$$= 16 + (20)$$
$$= (?)$$

Answers for (?) in Example 1.

a) 80

b) 100, 1100

c) 9, 4, 4, 74

d) 12, 12, 159

e) -5, 16

f) 16, 36

Exercise Set 1.9

Evaluate each expression:

1) $-2 - [3 \cdot (-4)]$ 2) $4 + 8 \cdot (-2)$

3) $4 \cdot 3 + (-6)$ 4) $-13 + (-52) \div (-13)$

5) $-(-5) \cdot 0 + 7$ 6) $-4 + 0 \div (-5)$

7) $-2 + (-3) \cdot 4$ 8) $10 \cdot [2 + (-3)] \div (-5)$

9) $-15 \div [2 - (-1)] \cdot (-3)$ 10) $3 \cdot [(-4) - 2]$

Evaluate each expression for the values given.

11) $2a + 15$ when $a = 10$

12) $4x^2 - 20$ when $x = 5$

13) $4m^2 + 3m$ when $m = (-3)$

14) $-9w - 1$ when $w = 9$

15) $(x + 1)^2$ when $x = 7$

16) $a^2 - c^2$ when $a = 6$ and $c = 3$

17) $a^2b^2 + ab$ when $a = (-2)$ and $b = 3$

18) $3d^2 - 2c^2$ when $d = -3$ and $c = -2$

19) $(4a + b) - (3a - b)$ when $a = 5$ and $b = (-1)$

20) $2ab(a + b)^2$ when $a = 2$ and $b = 3$

Answers for Exercise Set 1.9

1)	10	2)	-12	3)	6	4)	-9
5)	7	6)	-4	7)	-14	8)	2
9)	15	10)	-18	11)	35	12)	80
13)	27	14)	-82	15)	64	16)	27
17)	30	18)	19	19)	3	20)	300

Exercise Set 1.10 Properties of the Real Number System

Summary:

> **Commutative Property of Addition**
> If **a** and **b** represent any two real numbers, then
> $$a + b = b + a$$
>
> **Commutative Property of Multiplication**
> If **a** and **b** represent any two real numbers, then
> $$a \cdot b = b \cdot a$$
>
> **Associative Property of Addition**
> If **a, b,** and **c** represent any three real numbers, then
> $$(a + b) + c = a + (b + c)$$
>
> **Associative Property of Multiplication**
> If **a, b,** and **c** represent any three real numbers, then
> $$(a \cdot b) \cdot c = a \cdot (b \cdot c)$$
>
> **Distributive Property**
> If **a, b,** and **c** represent any three real numbers, then
> $$a(b + c) = ab + ac$$

➡**NOTE:** Commutative property: change in order
Associative property: change in grouping
Distributive property: two operations, multiplication and division

Example 1 **Name the following properties.**
Property
a) $(p \cdot q) \cdot r = p \cdot (q \cdot r)$
b) $7 + 5 = 5 + 7$
c) $5 + (3 + 4) = 5 + (4 + 3)$
d) $(m)(n) = (n)(m)$
e) $5 \cdot (9 + 15) = (5 \cdot 9) + (5 \cdot 15)$
f) $(1/2 + 3/4) + 7/16 = 1/2 + (3/4 + 7/16)$

Solution:

a) Associative property of multiplication
b) Commutative property of addition
c) Commutative property of addition
d) Commutative property of multiplication
e) Distributive property
f) Associative property of addition

➡**NOTE:** The associative property does not hold for subtraction or division.

For example,
$$(4 - 1) - 3 \neq 4 - (1 - 3) \text{ and } (8 \div 4) \div 2 \neq 8 \div (4 \div 2).$$

The commutative property does not hold for subtraction or division.
For example,
$$4 - 6 \neq 6 - 4 \text{ and } 6 \div 3 \neq 3 \div 6.$$

Exercise Set 1.10

Name the property illustrated.
1) $(a \cdot b) \cdot c = a \cdot (b \cdot c)$
2) $(-7) \cdot (-6) = (-6) \cdot (-7)$
3) $^2/_{32} \cdot (4 + 9) = (^2/_{32} \cdot 4) + (^2/_{32} \cdot 9)$
4) $0.7 + 1.5 = 1.5 + 0.7$
5) $m(7 \cdot 5) = m(5 \cdot 7)$
6) $(2 + 6) + 3 = 2 + (6 + 3)$
7) $a(b + c) = (a \cdot b) + (a \cdot c)$
8) $(2 + 6) + 3 = (6 + 2) + 3$
9) $e + f = f + e$
10) $8 \div 4 = 4 \div 8$

Complete each property.
11) Associative property of addition: $6 + (8 + 2) =$
12) Distributive property: $x(7 + 5) =$
13) Commutative property: $t + q =$
14) Associative property of multiplication: $(^3/_4 \cdot {}^8/_9) \cdot {}^2/_3 =$
15) Commutative property of multiplication: $(3)(-2) =$
16) Distributive property: $4(w + 13) =$
17) Associative property of addition: $x + (y + z) =$
18) Cummutative property of addition: $y + z =$
19) Associative property of multiplication: $0.5 \cdot (0.4 \cdot 1.9) =$
20) Commutative property of multiplication: $(-2.7)(1.5) =$

Answers for Exercise Set 1.10
1) Associative property of multiplication
2) Commutative property of multiplication
3) Distributive property
4) Commutative property of addition
5) Commutative property of multiplication
6) Associative property of addition
7) Distributive property
8) Commutative property of addition
9) Commutative property of addition
10) No answer; Commutative property does not hold for subtraction or division.
11) $6 + (8 + 2) = (6 + 8) + 2$
12) $x(7 + 5) = (x \cdot 7) + (x \cdot 5)$

13) t + q = q + t
14) $(^3/_4 \cdot \, ^8/_9) \cdot \, ^2/_3 = \, ^3/_4 \cdot (^8/_9 \cdot \, ^2/_3)$
15) (3) (-2) = (-2) (3)
16) 4(w + 13) = (4 • w) + (4 • 13)
17) x + (y + z) = (x + y) + z
18) y + z = z + y
19) 0.5 • (0.4 • 1.9) = (0.5 • 0.4) • 1.9
20) (-2.7)(1.5) = (1.5)(-2.7)

Practice Test Chapter 1.

1)   Consider the set of numbers:
$\{-9, 156, -2^1/_3, 0.5, \sqrt{7}, 6, -2^7/_{16}\}$

List those that are:
a) Integers.
b) Real Numbers.
c) Natural Numbers.
d) Rational Numbers.

2) Insert either <, >, or = in the space provided to make each expression true.
a) $-^3/_4$? $-^1/_4$ b) 8   ? |-14|

Evaluate each expression:

3) -1 - (- 5)   4) (-2)(-3)(-4)   5) -42 + 30
6) -5 + 23   7) 2 + 3 • 7   8) 0 ÷ [2(7 + 5)]
9) -21 ÷ (-3)   10) -1 + 6 - 10   11) $^{-5}/_4 ÷ \, ^{-3}/_4$
12) $(^{-2}/_3)^4$ 13) -2.8 + (-5.3)   14) 4[8-2(5-3) + 1]

15) Write (1.2)(1.2)(1.2) •a•a•a•b in exponential form.
16) Write 5^2 • 3 • m^4 n in factored form,

Evaluate each expression for the values given.
17) w^3 - w + 5, when w = 3
18) $x^2 + 2xy + y^2$, when x = -2 and y = 5

Name the property illustrated.
19) 5 + (x + 3) = 5 + (3 + x)
20) 4(x + y) = 4x + 4y

Answers for Practice Test Chapter 1.

1)   a) {-9, 6, 156}
        b) $\{-9, -2^7/_{16}, -2^1/_3, 0.5, \sqrt{7}, 6, 156\}$
        c) {6, 156}
        d) $\{-9, -2^7/_{16}, -2^1/_3, 0.5, 6, 156\}$

2) a) $-3/4 < -1/4$ b) $8 < |-14|$

3) 4   4) -24

5) -12   6) 18

7) 23   8) 0

9) 7   10) -5

11) $5/3$ 12) $16/81$

13) -8.1   14) 20

15) $(1.2)^3 a^3 b$ 16) $5 \cdot 5 \cdot 3 \cdot m \cdot m \cdot m \cdot m \cdot n$

17) 29   18) 9

19) Commutative property of addition

20) Distributive property

Chapter 2   Solving Linear Equations

Section 2.1 Combining Like Terms

Variables are letters used to represent numbers.

An **Algebraic Expression** is a collection of numbers, variables, grouping symbols, and operation symbols.

The word **Terms** is used when discussing the parts of an algebraic expression that are added or subtracted.

The numerical part of a term is called its **numerical coefficient** or simply coefficient.

Like Terms are terms that have the same variable with the same exponent.

Example 1   Determine if there are any like terms in each algebraic expression.
a) $3x - y + 2x$
b) $7x^2 - 3x + x^2 - 4 + x$
c) $x^2y - xy + xy^2 - 2x^2y$
d) $a^2 - ab + 3$

Solution:

a) $3x$ and $2x$ are like terms.
b) $7x^2$ and x^2 are like terms.
   $-3x$ and x are like terms.
c) x^2y and $-2x^2y$ are like terms.
d) No like terms.

Summary:

To combine like terms
1. Determine which terms are like terms.
2. Add or subtract the coefficients of the like terms.
3. Multiply the number found in (2) by the common variables.

Example 1   Combine like terms: 12a - 9a.

Solution: a) Determine the like terms: 12a and -9a.
                   b) Add or subtract the coefficients of the like terms; 12 - 9 = 3
                      therefore 12a - 9a = 3a.

Example 2   Combine like terms: 3x + 2y - 3x.

Solution: a) Determine the like terms: 3x and (?).
                   b) Add or subtract the coefficients of the like terms; 3 - 3 = 0
                      therefore 3x + 2y - 3x = 0x + 2y = 2y.

Answer for Example 2a.   -3x

Example 3   Combine like terms: 3 - 5mn + 2.

Solution: a) Determine the like terms: 3 and (?).
                   b) Add or subtract the coefficients of the like terms; 3 + 2 = 5
                      therefore 3 - 5mn + 2 = -5mn + (?).

Answer for (?) in Example 3. a) 2   b) 5

Example 4   Combine like terms: $7y^2 + 4y - 6 - 9y^2 - 2y + 7$.

Solution: a) Determine the like terms: $7y^2$ and $-9y^2$
                                                  4y and (?)
                                                  -6 and (?)
                   b) Add or subtract the coefficients of the like terms;
                               7 - 9 = (?)
                               4 - 2 = (?)
                              -6 + 7 = (?)
                      therefore $7y^2 + 4y - 6 - 9y^2 - 2y + 7 = -2y^2 + 2y + (?)$.

Answers for (?) in Example 4.   a) -2y , 7
                                     b) -2 , 2 , 1
                                     c) 1

Summary:

┌───┐
│ **Distributive Property**   │
│ For any real numbers **a, b,** and **c,** │
│   **a(b + c) = ab + ac**   │
└───┘

Example 5
     Use the distributive property to remove parentheses.
               a) 4(x + 10)   b) -3(m - 4)

Solution: a) $4(x + 10) = (4 \cdot x) + (4 \cdot 10) = 4x + (?)$

              b) $-3(m - 4) = (-3) \cdot (?) + (-3) \cdot (-4) = -3x + (?)$

Answers for (?) in Example 5.

              a) 40   b) m , 12

Summary:

> The Distributive property can be expanded as follows:
> $$a(b + c + d + \ldots + n) = ab + ac + ad + \ldots + an$$

Example 6

Use the distributive property to remove parentheses.

              a) $-5(3x^2 - 2x - 7)$ b) $7(y^2 - 4y + 3)$

Solution:

a) $-5(3x^2 - 2x - 7)$ $= -5(3x^2 + (-2x) + (-7))$
                           $= (-5)(3x^2) + (-5)(-2x) + (-5)(-7)$
                           $= -15x^2 + (?)x + (?)$

b) $7(y^2 - 4y + 3)$ $= 7(y^2 + (-4y) + 3)$
                           $= (7)(y^2) + (7)(-4y) + (7)(3)$
                           $= (?)y^2 + (?)y + 21$
                           $= 7y^2 - 28y + 21$

Answers for (?) in Example 6.

              a) 10, 35   b) 7, -28

Summary

> When no sign or a plus sign precedes parentheses, the parentheses may be removed without having to change the expression inside the parentheses.
>
> When a minus sign precedes, the signs of all the terms within the parentheses are changed when the parentheses are removed.

Example 7   Remove parentheses.

              a) $(ab - 4)$ b) $-(ab - 4)$ c) $-(x - y)$ d) $(4m - n)$

Solution: a) $(ab - 4) = ab - 4$
              b) $-(ab - 4) = -ab + 4$
              c) $-(x - y) = -x + y$
              d) $(4m - n) = 4m - n$

Summary:

> **To Simplify an Expression means to**
> 1) Remove parentheses when present by using the distributive law.
> 2) Combine like terms.

Example 8   Simplify
a) $7 + (m - 10)$ b) $14y - 5(x - y)$

Solution:

a) $7 + (m - 10) = 7 + m - 10$ distributive property
$ = m - 3$ combine like terms

b) $14y - 5(x - y)$ $= 14y - 5x + (?)y$ distributive property
$ = -5x + (?)y$ combine like terms

Answers for (?) in Example 8.
b) 5 , 19

Exercise Set 2.1

Combine like terms.
1) $15x - 3x$ 2) $5a - 12a$ 3) $2a - 5a + 6a$
4) $a^2b \ 3a^2b$ 5) $7x^2y - 2xy^2 - 4x^2y$ 6) $2x - y + 3x$
7) $3y - 4y + 5y$ 8) $5x - 8 + x + 3x$ 9) $3 - 5a + a - 2$

Use distributive property to remove parentheses.
10) $-3(x - 5)$ 11) $3(2x^2 - 4x + 5)$
12) $5(a + 6)$ 13) $8 + (a - b)$
14) $5 - (x - y)$ 15) $2(x - y) + 3$

Simplify each expression.
16) $3(a - 2x) + 5x$ 17) $-2(2x - b) - 3x$
18) $(R - S) - 3S$ 19) $8a - 3[b - 2(3a - b)]$
20) $4(m + 2n) + 2(m + 5n)$

Answers for Exercise Set 2.1
1) $12x$ 2) $-7a$ 3) $3a$
4) $-2a^2b$ 5) $3x^2y - 2xy^2$ 6) $5x - y$
7) $4y$ 8) $9x - 8$ 9) $-4a + 1$
10) $-3x + 15$ 11) $6x^2 - 12x + 15$ 12) $5a + 30$
13) $a - b + 8$ 14) $-x + y + 5$ 15) $2x - 2y + 3$
16) $3a - x$ 17) $-7x + 2b$ 18) $R - 4S$
19) $26a - 9b$ 20) $6m + 18n$

Section 2.2 Addition Property

Summary:

> An **Equation** is two algebraic expressions joined by the equal sign.
>
> A **Linear Equation** in one variable is an equation of the form
> **ax + b = c** for real numbers a, b, and c, c ≠ 0.
>
> A **Solution** of an equation is the number or numbers that make the
> equation a true statement.

Example 1 Consider the equation 5x + 2 = 12.
   Determine whether
         a) -2 is a solution or   b) 2 is a solution.

Solution:

   a) Check x = -2 $5x + 2 = 12$
                        $5(?) + 2 = 12$
                        $-10 + 2 = 12$
      Not a true statement: $-8 = 12$
      -2 is not a solution.

   b) Check x = 2 $5x + 2 = 12$
                        $5(?) + 2 = 12$
                        $10 + 2 = 12$
      This is a true statement: $12 = 12$
      2 is a solution.

Answers for (?) in Example 1.   a) -2   b) 2

Summary:

> *Addition Property*
> If **a = b**, then **a + c = b + c** for any real numbers **a, b,** and **c.**
>
> Since subtraction is defined in terms of addition, the addition property
> also allows us to subtract the same number from both sides of the
> equation.

Example 2 Solve each equation.
         a) x + 4 = 9   b) x - 3 = 4
         c) x - $^1/_2$ = 2   d) 0.3 - x = -0.4

Solution:

a)
$$x + 4 = 9$$
$$x + 4 + (-4) = 9 + (-4) \qquad \text{Add (-4) to both sides of equation.}$$
$$x + 0 = 5$$
$$x = 5 \qquad \textit{Answer}$$

b)
$$x - 3 = 4$$
$$x - 3 + (?) = 4 + (?) \qquad \text{Add (?) to both sides of equation.}$$
$$x + 0 = 7$$
$$x = 7 \qquad \textit{Answer}$$

c)
$$x - {}^1\!/_2 = 2$$
$$x - {}^1\!/_2 + (?) = 2 + (?) \qquad \text{Add (?) to both sides of equation.}$$
$$x + 0 = 2^1\!/_2$$
$$x = 2^1\!/_2 \qquad \textit{Answer}$$

d)
$$0.3 + x = -0.4$$
$$0.3 + (?) + x = -0.4 + (?) \qquad \text{Add (?) to both sides of equation.}$$
$$0 + x = -0.7$$
$$x = -0.7 \qquad \textit{Answer}$$

Answers for (?) in Example 2.   b) 3   c) $^1\!/_2$ d) -0.3

Exercise Set 2.2

Solve each equation, and check your solution.

1) $2 + x = -5$	2) $8 = x + 5$
3) $m + 4 = 5$	4) $-5 = m - 2$
5) $x + {}^2\!/_4 = {}^3\!/_4$	6) $y - {}^1\!/_3 = {}^{-2}\!/_3$
7) $^{-3}\!/_2 = t - {}^3\!/_2$	8) $-10 = 5 + r$
9) $-7 + x = 0$	10) $x + 1.4 = 2.3$
11) $7.0 = x - 1.6$	12) $a - 2.4 = 9.2$

Answers for Exercise Set 2.2

1) -7	2) 3	3) 1	4) -3
5) 1	6) $-^1\!/_3$	7) 0	8) -15
9) 7	10) 0.9	11) 8.6	12) 11.6

Section 2.3 The Multiplication Property

Summary:

> Multiplication Property
> If $a = b$, then $a \cdot c = b \cdot c$ for any numbers **a, b, and c.**
>
> The Multiplication Property can be used to solve equations of the form
> $ax = b$.

Example 1   Solve each equation:

a) $42 = 6x$ b) $11x = 33$
c) $x/5 = -2$ d) $m/6 = -4$
e) $2/3 w = 4$ f) $a/10 = 3.14$

Solution:

a) $42 = 6x$
$\frac{1}{6} \cdot 42 = \frac{1}{6} \cdot 6x$ Multiply both sides of equation by $\frac{1}{6}$.
$\frac{1}{6} \cdot 42 = \frac{1}{6} \cdot 6x$ Associative property of multiplication.
$7 = 1x$
$7 = x$ *Answer*

b) $11x = 33$
$(?) \cdot 11x = (?) \cdot 33$ Multiply both sides of equation by (?).
$1x = 3$
$x = 3$ *Answer*

c) $x/5 = -2$
$(?) \cdot x/5 = (?) \cdot (-2)$ Multiply both sides of equation by (?).
$1x = -10$
$x = -10$ *Answer*

d) $m/6 = -4$
$(?) \cdot m/6 = (?) (-4)$ Multiply both sides of equation by (?).
$1m = -24$
$m = -24$ *Answer*

e) $2/3 w = 4$
$(?) \cdot 2/3 w = (?) \cdot 4$ Multiply both sides of equation by (?).
$1w = 6$
$w = 6$ *Answer*

f) $a/10 = 3.14$
$(?) \cdot a/10 = (?) (3.14)$ Multiply both sides of equation by (?).
$1a = 31.4$
$a = 31.4$ *Answer*

Answers for (?) in Example 1.

b) $1/11$ c) 5   d) 6   e) $3/2$ f) 10

Summary:

> Since division can be defined in terms of multiplication (a/b means $a \cdot 1/b$) the multiplication property also allows us to divide both sides of an equation by the same nonzero number.

Example 2   Solve the equation -x = 18.

Solution: -x = 18 means that -1x = 18.

$$-1x = 18$$
$$(?)\,(-1x) = (?)\,(18)$$
$$1x = -18$$
$$x = 18 \qquad \textit{Answer}$$

Answer for (?) in Example 2. $^{-1}/_{18}$

➡**NOTE:**

For any real number a, a ≠ 0

If   -x = a

then x = -a

Examples:

-x = 7	-x = -2
x = -7	x = -(-2)
	x = 2

Exercise Set 2.3

Solve each equation, and check your solution.

1) 2x = 8	2) -3x = -15	3) 12x = -48
4) 4 = $^x/_7$	5) 3 = $^x/_{-8}$	6) -15 = $^x/_8$
7) $^x/_5$ = 7.8	8) $^3/_4$x = -2	9) $^{-5}/_3$x = -10
10) $^x/_{-3}$ = -4	11) $^x/_2$ = $^{-5}/_3$	12) -x = 4
13) -x = -3.14	14) 3x = $^{-1}/_4$	15) 12x = 144
16) 108 = -9x	17) 478 = -x	18) 625 = 5x

Answers for Exercise Set 2.3

1) 4	2) 5	3) -4
4) 28	5) -24	6) -120
7) 39.0	8) $^{-8}/_3$	9) 6
10) 12	11) $^{-10}/_3$	12) -4
13) 3.14	14) $^{-1}/_{12}$	15) 12
16) -12	17) -478	18) 125

Section 2.4 Solving Linear Equations with a variable on only one side of the equation.

Summary:

> To Solve Linear Equations with a Variable on Only One Side of the
> Equal Sign:
> 1) Use the distributive property to remove parentheses.
> 2) Combine like terms on the same side of the equal sign.
> 3) Use the addition property to obtain an equation with the term
>   containing the variable on one side of the equal sign and a constant
>   on the other side. This will result in an equation of the form **ax = b.**
> 4) Use the multiplication property to isolate the variable. This will give
>   an answer of the form $^x/_a$ **= b or lx = $^b/_a$.**
> 5) Check the solution in the original equation.

Example 1 Solve the equation $4x + 1 = 9$.
Solution: We will follow the outline stated above. Since the equation contains no
              parentheses and no like terms to combine, we start at step 3.

(Step 3)
$$4x + 1 = 9$$
$$4x + 1 + (-1) = 9 + (-1) \quad \text{Add (-1) to both sides of equation.}$$
$$4x + 0 = 8$$
$$4x = 8$$

(Step 4)
$$\tfrac{1}{4} \cdot 4x = 8 \cdot \tfrac{1}{4} \quad \text{Multiply both sides of equation by } \tfrac{1}{4}.$$
$$1x = 2$$
$$x = 2 \quad \textit{Answer}$$

(Step 5)
$$\text{Check: } 4x + 1 = 9$$
$$4(2) + 1 = 9$$
$$8 + 1 = 9$$
$$9 = 9 \quad \textit{True}$$

Example 2 Solve the equation $-8 = 3x - 25$.
Solution:
$$-8 = 3x - 25$$
(Step 3)
$$-8 + (?) = 3x - 25 + (?) \quad \text{Add (?) to both sides of equation.}$$
$$17 = 3x + O$$
$$17 = 3x$$

(Step 4)
$$(?) \cdot 17 = (?)3x \quad \text{Multiply both sides of equation by (?).}$$
$$^{17}/_3 = 1x$$
$$^{17}/_3 = x \quad \textit{Answer}$$

(Step 5)   Check: $-8 = 3x - 25$

$$-8 = 3 \left(^{17}/_3\right) - 25$$
$$-8 = {}^{51}/_3 - 25$$
$$-8 = (?) - 25$$
$$-8 = (?) \qquad \textbf{\textit{True}}$$

Answers for (?) in Example 2.

Step 3) 25   Step 4) $^1/_3$ Step 5) 17, -8

Example 3   Solve the equation $6x - 7 + 3x = 20$.

Solution: Since the left side of the equation has two like terms containing the variable x, we will first combine like terms.

(Step 2) $6x - 7 + 3x = 20$ Combine like terms.
                $9x - 7 = 20$

(Step 3) $9x - 7 + (?) = 20 + (?)$ Add (?) to both sides of equation.
                $9x + 0 = 27$
                $9x = 27$

(Step 4) $(?) \bullet 9x = 27 \bullet (?)$ Multiply both sides of equation by (?).
                $1x = 3$
                $x = 3$ **_Answer_**

(Step 5) Check:

$$6x - 7 + 3x = 20$$
$$6(?) - 7 + 3(?) = 20$$
$$18 - 7 + 9 = 20$$
$$20 = 20 \qquad \textbf{\textit{True}}$$

Answers for (?) in Example 3.

Step 3) 7   Step 4) $^1/_9$ Step 5) 3

Example 4   Solve the Equation $7x - 2(5 + 4x) = 8$.
Solution: Are there parentheses in the equation? ...yes.

(Step 1) $7x - 2(5 + 4x) = 8$ Use distributive property.
                $7x - 10 - 8x = 8$

Are there like terms on the same side of the equation? ...yes.

(Step 2) $7x - 10 - 8x = 8$ Combine like terms.
                $-1x - 10 = 8$

(Step 3)   -1x - 10 = 8
                    -1x - 10 + (?) = 8 + (?)   Add (?) to both sides of equation.
                           -1x = 18

(Step 4)   (?) • (-1x) = 18 • (?)   Multiply both sides of equation by (?).
                            1x = -18
                             x = -18   *Answer*

(Step 5)   Check:
                    7x - 2(5 + 4x) = 8
                7(-18) - 2(5 + 4(-18)) = 8
                   -126 - 2(5 + (-72)) = 8
                        -126 - 2(?) = 8
                        -126 + (?) = 8
                               8 = 8   *True*

Answers for (?) in Example 4.
         Step 3) 10   Step 4) (-1)   Step 5) (-67), 134

Example 5   Solve the equation 5x - 3(2 + 3x) = 6.
Solution: 5x - 3(2 + 3x) = 6
                   5x - 6 - 9x = 6   Property (?)
                      -4x - 6 = 6   Combine (?)
                  -4x - 6 + 6 = 6 + 6   Add (?) to both sides of equation.
                     -4x + 0 = 12
                        -4x = 12
               $^{-1}/_4$ • (-4x) = $^{-1}/_4$ • 12   Multiply both sides of equation by (?).
                         1x = -3
                          x = -3   *Answer*

Check: 5x - 3(2 + 3x) = 6
              5(?) - 3(2 + 3(?)) = 6
              -15 - 3(2 + (-9)) = 6
                 -15 - 3(-7) = 6
                 -15 + (?) = 6
                        6 = 6   *True*

Answers for (?) in Example 5.
         Distributive,   like terms,   6, $^{-1}/_4$,   (-3),   21

Exercise Set 2.4
         Solve each equation.
         1) 3x + 5 = 14   2) 8x - 9 = 47
         3) 2x + 4 + 3x = 19   4) -5 = 2x - 3
         5) -5 = 3x + 1 - 2x   6) 6x - 3 - 8x = 5 - 4
         7) 2x + 1 = -7   8) $-^2/_3$ x - 5 = 7
         9) 0.4 - 0.3x = -1.4   10) -3x + 7 = -4

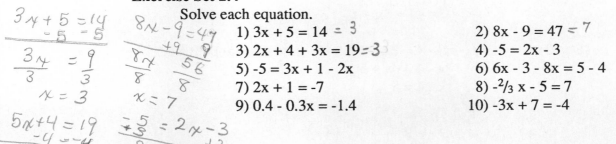

11) $5 = 3x - 4$ 12) $-1.1x + 4.2 = -1.3$
13) $6x - 5x - 5 = 11$ 14) $4 = 2x - x + 5$
15) $x -(2 - 3x) = -4$ 16) $8 = 2(x - 3) - (x - 2)$
17) $3(x - 1) - x = -7$ 18) $5(x + 1) - (4x + 3) = 14$
19) $-22 = 4x + 5(4 - 5x)$ 20) $6x + 2(3 - 8x) = -14$

Answers for Exercise Set 2.4

1) 3	2) 7	3) 3	4) -1
5) -6	6) -2	7) -4	8) -18
9) 6	10) $^{11}/_3$	11) 3	12) 5
13) 16	14) -1	15) $-^1/_2$	16) 12
17) -2	18) 12	19) 2	20) 2

Exercise Set 2.5

**Solving Linear Equations with variables on both sides of the equation.
Summary:**

> 1) Use the distributive property to remove parentheses.
> 2) Combine like terms on the same side of the equal sign.
> 3) Use the addition property to rewrite the equation with all terms containing the variable on one side of the equal sign. It may be necessary to use the addition property a number of times to accomplish this. Repeated use of the addition property will eventually result in an equation of the form **ax = b.**
> 4) Use the multiplication property to isolate the variable. This will give an answer of the form **x = some number.**
> 5) Check the solution in the original equation.

Example 1 Solve the equation $3x - 4 = 2x + 5$.
Solution: In solving this equation, use the procedure outlined above.

$$3x - 4 = 2x + 5$$

Does Step 1 as outlined by the author apply? ...No.
Does Step 2 apply? ...No.

Since the first two steps are not necessary,
start at Step 3.

$$3x - 4 = 2x + 5$$

(Step 3) $3x+(-2x) - 4 = 2x + (-2x)+5$ Add (-2x) to both sides of equation.
$1x - 4 = 0x + 5$
$1x - 4 = 5$

(Step 3) $1x - 4 + (?) = 5 + (?)$ Add (?) to both sides of equation.
            $1x + 0 = 9$
            $1x = 9$
            $x = 9$ *Answer*

(Step 5)   Check:
            $3x - 4 = 2x + 5$
            $3(?) - 4 = 2(?) + 5$
            $27 - 4 = 18 + 5$
            $23 = 23$ *True*

Answers for (?) in Example 1.
    Step 3) 4   Step 5) 9

Example 2   Solve the equation $5x - 2 - x = 4 - 3x - 27$.
Solution: Refering to the steps outlined by the author
    Does Step 1 apply? ...No.
    Does Step 2 apply? ...Yes.
    Start at Step 2.

(Step 2) $5x - 2 - x = 4 - 3x - 27$
                $4x - 2 = -3x - 23$ Combine like terms.

(Step 3) $4x + 3x - 2 = -3x + 3x - 23$ Add (3x) to both sides
                $7x - 2 = 0x - 23$ of equation.
                $7x - 2 = -23$

(Step 3) $7x - 2 + (?) = -23 + (?)$ Add (?) to both sides of equation.
                $7x + 0 = -21$
                $7x = -21$
(Step 4) $(?) \cdot 7x = (?) \cdot -21$ Multiply both sides of equation by (?).
                $1x = -3$
                $x = -3$ *Answer*

(Step 5)   Check:
            $5x - 2 - x = 4 - 3x - 27$
            $5(?) - 2 - (?) = 4 - 3(?) - 27$
            $-15 - 2 + 3 = 4 + 9 - 27$
            $-14 = -14$ *True*

Answers for (?) in Example 2.
    Step 3) 2   Step 4) $^1/_7$ Step 5) -3

Example 3   Solve the equation $10 - 7x = 4(11 - 6x)$.
Solution: Since parentheses exist, start at Step 1.

(Step 1) $10 - 7x = 4(11 - 6x)$

                        $10 - 7x = 44 - 24x$ Distributive property

Since step 2 does not apply, go to step 3.

(Step 3) $10 - 7x + 7x = 44 - 24x + 7x$ Add (?) to both sides of equation.

                    $10 + 0x = 44 - 17x$

                      $10 = 44 - 17x$

(Step 3) $10 + (?) = 44 + (?) - 17x$ Add (?) to both sides of equation.

                     $-34 = 0 - 17x$

                     $-34 = -17x$

(Step 4) $(?) \cdot (-34) = (?) \cdot (-17x)$ Multiply both sides of equation by (?).

                      $2 = 1x$

                      $2 = x$ *Answer*

(Step 5)   Check:

                $10 - 7x = 4(11 - 6x)$

                $10 - 7(?) = 4(11 - 6(?))$

                $10 - 14 = 4(11 - 12)$

                $10 - 14 = 4(?)$

                    $-4 = -4$ *True*

Answers for (?) in Example 2,

      Step 3) $7x$ Step 3) 44 Step 4) $-\frac{1}{17}$ Step 5) $2, -1$

Summary:

> **Conditional Equations** are equations with a single value solution.
> **Identities** are equations true for all values of x.

Example 4   Solve the equation $3x + 4 + 7x = 2(5x + 2)$.

Solution: $3x + 4 + 7x = 2(5x + 2)$

(Step 1) $3x + 4 + 7x = 10x + 4$ Distributive property

(Step 2) $10x + 4 = 10x + 4$ Combine like terms.

(Step 3) $10x + (?) = 10x + (?) + 4$ Add (?) to both sides of equation.

                   $4 = 4$

           $4 + (-4) = 4 + (-4)$ Add (-4) to both sides of equation.

               $0=0$

Answer for (?) in Example 4.   Step 3) $(-10x)$

      Since the same expression appears on both sides of the equal sign, the statement is true for all values of **x**. Example 4 is an **identity**.

Example 5 Solve the equation   5x + 9 = 5x - 15.

Solution: 5x + 9 = 5x - 15

Since step 1 and step 2 does not apply, go to step 3.

(Step 3)   5x + 9 = 5x - 15

5x + (?) + 9 = 5x + (?) - 15   Add (?) to both sides of equation.

9 = -15   False

Answer for (?) in Example 5.   Step 3)   (-5x)

When solving an equation if you obtain an obviously false statement as above, the equation has no solution.

No value of x will make the equation above a true statement.

Exercise Set 2.5

Solve each equation.

1) 5x = 3x - 4

2) 7x = 4x - 9

3) 6x + 7 = 3 + 8x

4) 7x - 8 = 8 - 9x

5) 16 - 7 = 3 + 8x

6) 13 - 11x - 17 = 5x + 4 - 10x

7) 4x + 5(4 - 5x) = -22

8) 7x + 5 = 3(3x + 5)

9) 3x - 2(2x - 7) = 2(3 + x) - 4

10) 6(3 - 4x) + 12 = 10x - 2(5 - 3x)

11) 2x + 19 - x = 8x + 3 - 7x

12) 5x - 8 = x

13) 7 - 9x - 12 = 3x + 5 - 8x

14) $3 \left(\frac{2}{3} + \frac{10}{3}x\right) = 5 \left(\frac{2}{5} + 2x\right)$

Answers for Exercise Set 2.5

1) -2	2) -3	3) 2	4) 1
5) $\frac{3}{4}$	6) $-\frac{4}{3}$	7) 2	8) -5
9) 4	10) 1	11) no solution	
12) 2	13) $-\frac{5}{2}$	14) all real numbers	

Section 2.6 Ratios and Proportions

Summary:

A **RATIO** is another name for a fraction. The ratio of **a** to **b** is written **a/b** or **a:b**. The **a** and **b** are the terms of the ratio.

Example 1   The nursing class at the Community College of the Finger Lakes consists of 3 males and 20 females.

a) Find the ratio of females to males.
b) Find the ratio of males to the entire class.
c) Find the ratio of males to females

Solution: a) $^{20}/_3$ **or** 20:3
b) $^{3}/_{23}$ **or** 3:23
c) $^{3}/_{20}$ **or** 3:20

Summary:

To Solve Ratio Problems
1) Multiply each term of the ratio by the variable.
2) Set the sum of each of the terms in (1) equal to the total amount.
3) Solve the resulting equation.
4) Answer the equations asked.

Example 2   Phil Smith divided $27,000 among his three nephews in the ratio 2:3:4. How much did each receive?

(Step 1)   Let 2x = 1st nephews share
3x = 2nd nephews share
4x = 3rd nephews share

(Step 2)
(1st nephews share) + (2nd nephews share) + (3rd nephews share) = total amount

2x   +   3x   +   4x   =   27,000

(Step 3)   9x = 27,000 x = 3,000

(Step 4)   The 1st nephew receives 2x or 2(3,000)   = $ 6,000
The 2nd nephew receives 3x or 3(3,000)   = $ 9,000
The 3rd nephew receives 4x or 4(3,000)   = $12,000

Total $27,000

Summary:

> A **proportion** is a special type of equation. It is a statement of equality between two ratios. One way of denoting a proportion is **a:b = c:d,** which is read "**a** is to **b** as **c** is to **d**." In this text we write proportions as
>
> $$a/b = c/d$$
>
> The **a** and **d** are referred to as the **extremes** and the **b** and **c** are referred to as the **means** of the proportion. One method that can be used in evaluating proportions is **cross-multiplication:**
>
> **Cross-Multiplication**
> If $a/b = c/d$ then ad = bc.

Example 3

Solve for x by cross-multiplying
$$-4/7 = x/21$$

$$\frac{-4}{7} = \frac{x}{21}$$
$$7x = -84$$
$$\frac{7x}{7} = \frac{-84}{7}$$
$$x = -12$$

Solution:
$$-4 \cdot (?) = (?) \cdot x$$
$$-84 = 7x$$
$$-84/(?) = x$$
$$-12 = x \qquad \textit{Answer}$$

Check:
$$-4/7 = (?)/21$$
$$-4/7 = -12/21$$
$$-4/7 = -4/7 \qquad \textit{True}$$

Answers for (?) in Example 3.   21,   7,   7,   (-12)

Summary:

> **To Solve Problems Using Proportions**
> 1) Represent the unknown quantity by a letter.
> 2) Set up the proportion by listing the given ratio on the left side of the equal sign and the unknown and other given quantity on the right side of the equal sign. When setting up the right side of the proportion the same respective quantities should occupy the same respective positions on the left and right. For example, an acceptable proportion might be
>
> given ratio   { miles/hour = miles/hour
>
> 3) Once the proportion is correctly written, drop the units and cross-multiply.
> 4) Solve the resulting equation.
> 5) Answer the questions asked.

➡**Note** that the ratios must have the same units. For example, if one ratio is given in miles/hour and the second ratio is given in feet/hour, one of the ratios must be changed before setting up the proportion.

Example 4 Roselinde Mandery used 10 gallons of gas on a 180 mile trip. How many gallons of gas can she expect to use on a 300 mile trip?

Solution:

(Step l) Let x = gallons of gas

unknown

(Step 2) given ratio { $^{10\ \text{gallons}}/_{180\ \text{miles}} = {}^{x\ \text{gallons}}/_{300\ \text{miles}}$

given quantity

(Step 3) $^{10}/_{180} = {}^{x}/_{300}$

$(10) \cdot (300) = 180\ x$

(Step 4) $3000 = 180x$

$^{3000}/_{180} = x$

$16.7 = x$ (rounded value) ***Answer***

(Step 5) On a 300-mile trip approximately 16.7 gallons of gas will be used.

Example 5 Bob's Big M has a bargain price of 85 cents for three jars of grape jelly. How many jars could someone buy for $5.95.

Solution:

(Step l) Let x = number of jars of jelly

unknown

(Step 2) given ratio { $^{3\ \text{jars}}/_{85\ \text{price}} = {}^{x\ \text{jars}}/_{595\ \text{price}}$

given quantity

➡**Note:** The price should be either in all cents or dollars and cents.

(Step 3) $^{3}/_{85} = {}^{x}/_{595}$

$3 \cdot (?) = 85x$

(Step 4) $1785 = 85x$

$^{1785}/_{(?)} = x$

$21 = x$ ***Answer***

(Step 5) If 3 jars cost 85 cents then 21 jars will cost $5.95.

Answers for (?) in Example 3. Step 3) 595 ; Step 4) 85

Exercise Set 2.6

1) In the fifth grade at North Rose Wolcott School 5 students play trumpet, 6 students play guitar, 3 students play piano, and 18 students play no instrument. Assuming that no music student plays more than one instrument, write the following ratios.

a) The ratio of trumpet players to total students.
b) The ratio of guitar players to piano players.
c) The ratio of non-instrument playing students to
   piano players.
d) The ratio of piano players to total students.

2) The amount Mary Ann Giebner spends for food, rent, and clothing
   are in ratio 4:5:1. She spends an average of $450 a month for these
   items. What can she expect to spend for these items each year?

3) A Wayne County fruit farmer has 153 acres proportioned into five
   acres of apple trees to four acres of cherry trees. How many acres
   of each does he have?

4) Two numbers are in the ratio of 7 to 3. Their sum is 130. Find the
   numbers.

Solve for the variable by cross-multiplying

5) $^8/_x = {}^4/_5$ 6) $^x/_5 = {}^6/_4$

7) $^{15}/_{12} = {}^x/_9$ 8) $^{144}/_{36} = {}^{96}/_x$

Write a proportion that can be used to solve the equation.
Solve the equation and find the desired value.

9) The ratio of a man's weight on Mars compared to his weight on
   earth is 2:5. How much would a 210-pound man weigh on Mars?

10) The Rochester Red Wings won seven of its first 12 games. How
    many games would you expect it to win out of its first 36 games if
    the team continues to play with the same degree of success.

Answers for Exercise Set 2.6

1a) 5:32   b) 2:1   c) 6:1   d) 3:32

2) $180 food   3) 85 acres with apple trees
   $225 rent   68 acres with cherry trees
   $ 45 clothing

4) 39, 91   5) 10
6) $^{15}/_2$ 7) $^{45}/_4$
8) 24   9) 84 pounds
10) 21 games

Section 2.7 Inequalities In One Variable
Summary:

> The greater than symbol, $>$, and the less than symbol, $<$, were introduced in Section 1.2. The symbol $\geq$ means greater than or equal to and $\leq$ means less than or equal to. A mathematical expression containing one or more of these symbols is called an **inequality.** The direction of the symbol is sometimes called the **sense** of the inequality.
>
> ### Examples of inequalities in one variable
>
> $x + 3 < 5,$ $x + 4 \geq 2x - 6,$ $4 > -x + 3$
>
> To solve an inequality, we must get the variable by itself on one side of the inequality sign.

The same properties used previously to solve equations are used also for solving inequalities. These properties are stated formally below.

Properties Used to Solve Inequalities
For real numbers a, b, and c.

1) Addition property   If $a > b$, then $a + c > b + c$.

2) Subtraction property   If $a > b$, then $a - c > b - c$.

3) Multiplication property   If $a > b$ and $c < 0$, then $ac < bc$.

4) Division property   If $a > b$ and $c < 0$, then $^a/_c < ^b/_c$.

Example 1
Solve the inequality $x - 5 < 2$, and graph the solution on the real number line.
Solution: To solve this inequality we need to isolate the variable x.

$x - 5 < 2$
$x - 5 + 5 < 2 + 5$ add (?) to both sides of inequality
$x + 0 < 7$
$x < 7$

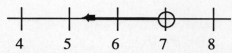

Unlike equations, inequalities have several answers. The solution $x < 7$ implies all the real numbers less than seven are solutions for the inequality $x - 5 < 2$.

Answer for (?) in Example 1.   5

Example 2   Solve the inequality -3 > 5 + x
Solution:
$$-3 > 5 + x$$
$$-3 + (?) > 5 + (?) + x \qquad \text{Add (?) to both sides of inequality}$$
$$-8 > 0 + x$$
$$-8 > x$$

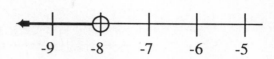

The solution is any real numbers greater than -8.

Answer for (?) in Example 2.   (-5)

Example 3   Solve the inequality 5x + 4 ≤ 19
Solution:
$$5x + 4 \quad \leq 19$$
$$5x + 4 + (?) \quad \leq 19 + (?) \qquad \text{Add (?) to both sides of inequality.}$$
$$5x + 0 \quad \leq 15$$
$$5x \leq 15$$
$${}^{5x}/_{(?)} \leq {}^{15}/_{(?)} \qquad \text{Divide both sides of inequality by (?)}$$
$$x \leq 3$$

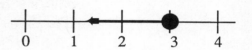

The solution is any real number less than or equal to 3.

Answers for (?) in Example 3.   (-4),   5

Summary:

> When an inequality is multiplied or divided by a negative number, the sense (direction) of the inequality changes.

Additional Properties Used to Solve Inequalities

5) If a > b and c < 0, then ac < bc.

6) If a > b and c < 0, then $^a/_c < {}^b/_c$.

c < 0 implies c is a negative number.
Notice the direction of the inequality changes.

Example 4   Solve the inequality -3x + 5 ≤ 14 and
graph the solution on the real number line.

Solution: $-3x + 5 \leq 14$

$-3x + 5 + (?) \leq 14 + (?)$ Add (?) to both sides of inequality.

$-3x + 0 \leq 9$

$-3x \leq 9$ Divide both sides of inequality by (-3).

$^{-3x}/_{-3} \leq \, ^{9}/_{-3}$

$x \geq -3$ Change the direction of the inequality symbol.

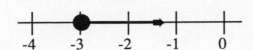

The solution is any real number greater than or equal to -3.

Answers for (?) in Example 4. (-5)

Example 5   Solve the inequality $6x + 7 > 3 + 8x$ and
graph the solution on the real number line.

Solution: $6x + 7 > 3 + 8x$

$6x + (-6x) + 7 > 3 + 8x + (-6x)$ Add (?) to both sides of inequality.

$0x + 7 > 3 + 2x$

$7 > 3 + 2x$

$7 + (?) > 3 + (?) + 2x$ Add (?) to both sides of inequality.

$4 > 0 + 2x$

$4 > 2x$

$^{4}/_{(?)} > \, ^{2x}/_{(?)}$ Divide both sides of inequality by (?).

$2 > x$

The solution is any real number less than 2.

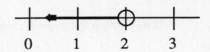

Answers for Example 5. (-6x), (-3), 2

Exercise Set 2. 7

Solve each inequality, and graph your solution on the real number line.

1) $x - 5 < 6$ 2) $x + 7 \leq 9$

3) $-2x < 10$ 4) $30 > 5x$

5) $^{2x}/_3 \geq 12$ 6) $27 \geq -3x$

7) $7 - x > 1$ 8) $2x - 10 \leq 2$

9) $-3x - 4 \geq 2x + 6$ 10) $^{x}/_4 + 5 \geq -6$

11) $3 - 5x < 2x + 6$ 12) $3x - 5 \leq 10$

13) $-2x + 1 > -3$ 14) $2x - 5 < -x + 6$

15) $3 - 2x \geq 5x + 5$ 16) $6x - 5 \leq -10x - 4$

17) $2x - 4 > 5x + 5$ 18) $-2x + 7 > -3$

19) $3(1 - 2x) < -2(x +3) -4$ 20) $3(x - 1) - 2(x+3) < 4x$

Answers for Exercise Set 2.7

1) $x < 11$

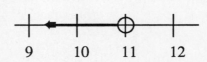

2) $x \leq 2$

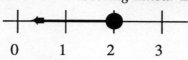

3) $x > -5$

4) $x < 6$

5) $x \geq 18$

6) $x < -9$

7) $x < 6$

8) $x \leq 6$

9) $x < -2$

10) $x \geq -44$

11) $x > {}^{-3}/_7$

12) $x \leq 5$

13) $x < 2$

14) $x < {}^{11}/_3$

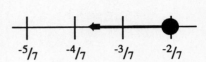

15) $x \leq {}^{-2}/_7$

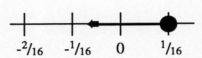

16) $x \leq {}^{1}/_{16}$

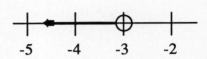

17) $x < -3$

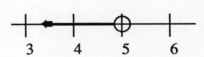

18) $x < 5$

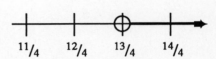

19) $x > {}^{13}/_4$

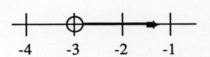

20) $x \geq -3$

Practice Test Chapter 2.

Use the distributive property to remove the parentheses.

1) $-5(4 - 7x)$ 2) $(x + y - 7z)$

Simplify where possible.

3) $4(a - 2b) + 5a$ 4) $2x - y + 3x + 7y$

5) $4a - 2b + 2b$ 6) $5x - 3x + 7 - 2x + 8x - 9$

Solve each equation.

7) $12 = x - 11$ 8) $x/_3 = 4$

9) $3.04 + x = 2.96$ 10) $6x - 33 = 27$

11) $-48 = 36x + 42$ 12) $5x - 7 = 7 - 9x$

13) $10 - 7x = 4(11 - 6x)$ 14) $3(2x-6) - 2(6x+4) = 5(x+8)$

Solve each inequality, and graph the solution on the real number line.

15) $7x - 3 < 18$ 16) $5x + 4 \leq 19$

17) $-3x - 5 < 4$ 18) $3x - 11 > 5(x - 1)$

19) Chris Lirosi spends $4,725.00 for tuition, housing, and food each semester. The amounts spent for these three items are in ratio 4:1:2. How much does she spend for each item?

20) A 6-foot man has a 4-foot shadow when a tree casts a 20-foot shadow. How tall is the tree?

Answers for Practice Test Chapter 2

1) -20 + 35x 2) x + y - 7z
3) 9a - 8b 4) 5x + 6y
5) 4a 6) 8x - 2
7) x = 23 8) x = 12
9) x = -0.08 10) x = 10
11) x = $-5/2$ 12) x = 1
13) x = 2 14) x = -6

15) x < 3

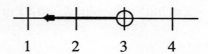

16) x ≤ 3

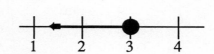

17) x > -3

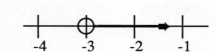

18) x < -3

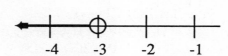

19) tuition = $2700.00   20) 30 feet
    housing = $ 675.00
    food = $1350.00

❖❖❖❖❖❖❖❖❖❖❖❖❖❖

Chapter 3 Formulas & Applications of Algebra

Section 3.1 Formulas

Summary:

> A Formula is an equation commonly used to express a specific physical concept mathematically. To solve any question using a formula, if all the quantities except one is given, substitute the quantities in the given formula and solve the equation for the unknown or missing quantity.

Formulas for Areas and Perimeters

Figure	Area	Perimeter
Square	$A = s^2$	$P = 4s$
Rectangle	$A = LW$	$P = 2L + 2W$
Parallelogram	$A = Lh$	$P = 2L + 2W$
Trapezoid	$A = \frac{1}{2}h(b_1 + b_2)$	$P = s_1 + s_2 + b_1 + b_2$
Triangle	$A = \frac{1}{2}bh$	$P = s_1 + s_2 + b$

Example 1   Find the perimeter of a rectangle when L = 7 feet and W = 5 feet.

Solution: Substitute 7 for L and 5 for W in the
formula for the perimeter of a triangle.

$$P = 2L + 2W$$
$$P = 2(7) + 2(5)$$
$$P = (?) + (?)$$
$$P = (?) \text{ feet}$$

Answers for (?) in Example 1.   14 , 10 , 24

Example 2   Find the length of a rectangle when the perimeter is 46.6 feet and the width is 13.3 feet.

Solution: Substitute 46.6 for P and 13.3 for W in the formula.

$$P = 2L + 2W$$
$$46.6 = 2L + 2(13.3)$$ Now solve the equation for L.
$$46.6 = 2L + 26.6$$
$$46.6 + (-26.6) = 2L + 26.6 + (-26.6)$$ Add (?) to both sides of equation.
$$20 = 2L + 0$$

$$20 \quad = 2L$$
$$^{20}/_2 \quad = {}^{2L}/_2$$
$$10 \quad = L$$

Divide both sides of equation by (?).

The length of the rectangle is 10 feet.

Answers for (?) in Example 2.   (-26.6) ,   2

Summary:

> **Circumference**, C, is the length (perimeter) of the curve that forms a circle.
>
> **Radius**, r, is the line segment from the center of the circle to any point on the circle.
>
> **Diameter** of a circle is a line segment through the center with both end points on the circle. Note that the diameter is twice the radius.
>
> Circle $A = \pi r^2$ $C = 2\pi r$
>
> **π has a value approximately 3.14.**

Example 3   Determine the area and circumference of a circle with a diameter of 24 inches.

Solution: The radius is half the diameter, $r = {}^{24}/_2 = 12$ inches.

$A = \pi r^2$	$C = 2\pi r$
$A = \pi \cdot r \cdot r$	$C = 2(3.14)(12)$
$A = (3.14)(12)(12)$	$C = 75.36$ inches
$A = 452.16$ square inches	

Example 4   How much interest would you pay if you borrowed $1200 at an annual interest rate of 9% for 6 months?

Let   i = interest,
      p = principal,
      r = the annual interest rate, and
      t = time.

To calculate interest use i = prt where r is expressed as a decimal and t is in years.

Solution: Rename 9%   9% = 0.09
      6 months = $^6/_{12}$ $^6/_{12}$ = 0.5
      i = prt
      i = (1200)(0.09)(0.5)
      i = $54

Summary:

Solving for a variable in a formula

Often in science, mathematics, or other courses you will be given an equation or formula solved for one variable and be asked to solve it for a different variable. To do this, treat each of the quantities, except the one you are solving for, as if they were constants. Then solve for the desired variable, by isolating it on one side of the equation, using the properties discussed previously.

Example 5   Solve the equation $C = 2\pi r$ for r.

Solution: We must get r by itself on one side of the equation.

$C = 2\pi r$

$C/_{2\pi} = {^{2\pi r}}/_{2\pi}$ Multiply both sides of equation by $^{1}/_{2\pi}$.

$C/_{2\pi} = r$ New Formula.

Example 6   Solve the equation $s = p + prt$ for t.

Solution: $s = p + prt$ Isolate the term with t on one side of equation.

$s + (-p) = p + (-p) + prt$ Add (?) to both sides of equation.

$s - p = 0p + prt$

$s - p = prt$

$^{s-p}/_{pr} = {^{prt}}/_{pr}$ Multiply both sides of equation by (?).

$^{s-p}/_{pr} = t$ New Formula.

Answers for (?) in Example 6. $(-p)$, $^{1}/_{pr}$

Example 7   Solve the equation $3x - 5y = 10$ for y.

Solution: $3x - 5y = 10$ Isolate the term with y on one side of equation.

$3x + (-3x) - 5y = 10 + (-3x)$ Add (?) to both sides of equation.

$0x - 5y = 10 - 3x$

$-5y = 10 - 3x$

$^{-5y}/_{-5} = {^{10-3x}}/_{-5}$ Multiply both sides of equation by (?).

$y = {^{10-3x}}/_{-5}$ New Formula.

Answers for (?) in Example 7. $(-3x)$, $^{-1}/_{5}$

Exercise Set 3.1

Use the formula to find the value of the indicated variable for values given.

     1) $i = prt$, find i when $p = \$250$, $r = 0.08$, and $t = 3$.

     2) $p = 4s$, find p when $s = 1.5$.

     3) $A = {^{1}}/_{2}bh$, find A when $b = 40$ and $h = 10$.

     4) $F = {^{9}}/_{5}C + 32$, find F when $C = 10$.

     5) $P = s_1 + s_2 + b$, find b when $P = 23$, $s_1 = 5$, and $s_2 = 8$.

6) $C = 2\pi r$, find C when $r = 10$.

7) $A = {}^1/_2 bh$, find h when $A = 30$, and $b = 6$.

8) $I = {}^E/_R$, find I when $E = 220$, and $R = 40$.

9) $A = ({}^{a}1 + {}^{a}2 + {}^{a}3)/3$, find ${}^{a}/_3$ when $A = 96$, $a_1 = 76$ and $a_2 = 85$.

10) $HP = {}^{D^2N}/_{2.5}$, find HP when $D = 3.5$, and $N = 4$.

Solve each equation for **y**, then find the value of **y** for the given value of **x**.

11) $-2x + 3y = 6$,   when $x = 12$.

12) $-x - 2y + 6 = 0$,   when $x = -20$.

13) $5y - 4x = 14$,   when $x = 5$.

14) $y + 2 = x$,   when $x = -19$.

15) $y - 4x = 1$,   when $x = {}^5/_4$.

16) $3x + y = 4$,   when $x = -2$.

17) $2x + y = 3$,   when $x = {}^{-1}/_2$.

18) $5x + 2y = 10$,   when $x = -6$.

19) $4x + y = 5$,   when $x = {}^1/_2$.

20) $2y - 3x = 15$,   when $x = 8$.

Solve for the variable indicated.

21) $V = LWH$, solve for W

22) $E = mc^2$, solve for m

23) $P = a + b + c$, solve for a

24) $a - 3 = by + c$, solve for b

Answers for Exercise Set 3.1

1) $60

2) 6

3) 200 square units

4) 50

5) 10

6) 62.8

7) 10 square units

8) 5.5

9) 127

10) 19 .6

11) $y = {}^{2x}/_3 + 2$; $y = 10$

12) $y = {}^{-1}/_2 x + 3$; $y = 13$

13) $y = {}^{(4x + 14)}/_5$; $y = {}^{34}/_5$

14) $y = x - 2$; $y = -21$

15) $y = 4x + 1$; $y = 6$

16) $y = -3x + 4$; $y = 10$

17) $y = -2x + 3$; $y = 4$

18) $y = {}^{-5x}/_2 + 5$; $y = 20$

19) $y = -4x + 5$; $y = 3$

20) $y = {}^{(3x + 15)}/_2$; $y = {}^{39}/_2$

21) $W = {}^V/_{LH}$

22) $m = {}^E/_{c^2}$

23) $a = P - b - c$

24) $b = {}^{(a - c - 3)}/_y$

Section 3.2 Changing Word Problems into Equations.

Summary:

In changing word problems into mathematical symbols one should recognize the words that imply mathematical operations.

+	-	x	÷
add	subtract	multiply	divided
more	less	product	quotient
increase	decrease	times	
sum	difference	of	
augmented	diminished		
exceed	minus		

Here are examples of statements represented as algebraic expressions.

Verbal	**Algebraic**
5 more than a number	$x + 5$
a number increased by 3	$x + 3$
7 less than a number	$x - 7$
a number decreased by 12	$x - 12$
twice a number	$2x$
the product of 6 and a number	$6x$
one-eighth of a number	$\frac{1}{8}x$ or $\frac{x}{8}$
a number divided by 3	$\frac{1}{3}x$ or $\frac{x}{3}$
4 more than twice a number	$2x + 4$
5 less than three times a number	$3x - 5$
3 times the sum of a number and 8	$3(x + 8)$

Example 1   Express each phrase as an algebraic expression.
   a) The sum of x and ten.
   b) a increased by b.
   c) Subtract the product of U and V from 20.
   d) One tenth of x decreased by 15.

Solution: a) x + 10
             b) a + b
             c) 20 - UV
             d) $^1/_{10}$x - 15 or 0.lx - 15

Example 2   For each relationship, select a variable to represent one quantity
               and express the other quantity in terms of the first.

               a) Len Malinowski's salary is seventy-five dollars more than Ike
                  Dunham's salary.
               b) The sum of two numbers is sixty.
               c) Sherm Hunt is twice as old as Sandy Brown.
               d) At the College Book Rack a notebook is seventeen cents less than
                  five times the cost of a ballpoint pen.

Solution: a) x   Ike Dunham's salary
               x + 75   Len Malinowski's salary

             b) x   lst number
                60 - x   2nd number

             c) x   Sandy Brown's age
                2x   Sherm Hunt's age

             d) x   Cost of a ballpoint pen
                5x - 17   Cost of a notebook

Summary:

> The word "**is**" in a verbal problem means "is equal to" and is repre-
> sented by an equal sign.

Example 3   Write as an equation.
               a) Twice the result of subtracting an unknown number from five is
                  eight.
               b) The sum of three numbers is 63. The first is twice the second and
                  the third is three times the first.
               c) One number is 7 more than another number. Find the two numbers
                  if three times the larger exceeds four times the smaller by 5.

Solutions:

             a)   Let x = unknown number
                            2(5 - x) = 8

             b)   Let x = 2nd number
                       Let 2x = 1st number

Let 3(2x) = 6x = 3rd number

(lst number) + (2nd number) + (3rd number) = 63

   2x   +   x   +   6x   = 63

c)   Let x = smaller number
        Let x + 7 = larger number

3 • (larger number) - 5   = 4 • (smaller number)
      3(x + 7) - 5   = 4x

Exercise Set 3.2

Express as an algebraic expression.

1) A number divided by -3.
2) 3 minus twice a number.
3) The quotient of a number and 2 decreased by 8.
4) The number of inches in x feet.
5) The total value of x dimes and y quarters.

Select a variable to represent one quantity, and express the second quantity in terms of the first.

6) One number is 9 less than another number.
7) Ten dollars divided between two people.
8) The new property assessment is 4 times the old property assessment.
9) My new salary is $2500 more than my old salary.
10) Two consecutive integers.
11) Donald Chapman is five years older than twice his brother's age.
12) The length of a rectangle is eleven feet more than twice the width of a rectangle.

Express as an equation.

13) If 3 is added to a number and then divided by 2, the result is 1.5.
14) The sum of three consecutive even integers is 36.
15) 15 is 30% of what number?
16) The length of a rectangle is 7 more than 3 times the width. The perimeter of the rectangle is 54.
17) A collection of nickles, dimes, and quarters is worth $5.30. There are two more dimes than nickles and four more quarters than dimes.
18) A rope 180 feet long is cut into three pieces such that the second piece is twice the length of the first piece and the third piece is three times the length of the second piece.
19) The number of cents in "n" nickles is 535.
20) One number is 8 less than 5 times another. The sum of the two numbers is -20.

Answers for Exercise Set 3.2

1) $x \div (-3)$ 2) $2x - 3$ 3) $(x \div 2) - 8$
4) $12x$ 5) $10x + 25y$

6) $x = $ 1st number
   $x - 9 = $ 2nd number

7) $x = $ 1st amount
   $10 - x = $ 2nd amount

8) $x = $ old assessment
   $4x = $ new assessment

9) $x = $ old salary
   $x + 2,500 = $ new salary

10) $x = $ 1st number
    $x + 1 = $ 2nd number

11) $x = $ brother's age
    $2x + 5 = $ Donald Chapman's age

12) $x = $ width
    $2x + 11 = $ length

13) $(x + 3)/2 = 1.5$

14) $n + n + 2 + n + 4 = 36$
15) $0.3x = 15$
16) $2(3x + 7) + 2x = 54$
17) $5x + 10(x + 2) + 25(x + 6) = 530$
18) $x + 2x + 3(2x) = 180$
19) $5n = 535$
20) $x + 5x - 8 = -20$

Section 3.3 Solving Application Problems

Transforming verbal problems into mathematical terms follow the outline stated below.

Summary:

> **To Solve an Application Problem**
> 1. Read the question carefully.
> 2. Determine which quantity you are being asked to find. Choose a letter to represent this unknown quantity. Write down exactly what this letter represents.
> 3. Write the word problem as an equation.
> 4. Solve the equation for the unknown quantity.
> 5. Answer the question or questions asked.
> 6. Check the solution.

Example 1 One number is 5 more than twice another and their sum is 23. What are the numbers?

Let $x = $ first number
Let $2x + 5 = $ second number

(first number) + (second number) = 23

Write the equation: $x + 2x + 5 = 23$

Solve the equation: $x + 2x + 5 = 23$

$$3x + 5 = 23$$
$$3x + 5 + (-5) = 23 + (-5)$$
$$3x = 18$$
$$x = {}^{(?)}/_3$$
$$x = 6$$

Answer the question: 1st number ... $x = 6$

2nd number ... $2x + 5 = 2(6) + 5 = 17$

Check: $6 + 17 = 23$

$23 = 23$ ***True***

Answer for (?) in Example 1)   18.

Example 2   A collection of nickels, dimes, and quarters is worth $21.75. There are twelve fewer nickels than dimes and as many quarters as there are nickels and dimes together. How many of each type of coin is there?

Let x = dimes   money value ... $5(x - 12)$
Let $x - 12$ = nickels   money value ... $10x$
Let $x + x - 12$ = quarters   money value ... $25(2x - 12)$

(money value nickels) + (money value dimes) + (money value quarters) = $21.75

Write the equation: $5(x - 12) + 10x + 25(2x - 12) = 2175$

Solve the equation: $5(x - 12) + 10x + 25(2x - 12) = 2175$

$$5x - 60 + 10x + 50x - 300 = 2175$$
$$(?)x - 360 = 2175$$
$$(?)x - 360 + 360 = 2175 + 360$$
$$(?)x = 2535$$
$$^{(?)x}/_{(?)} = {}^{2535}/_{(?)}$$
$$x = 39$$

Answer the question: nickels $x - 12 = 39 - 12 = 27$
dimes $x = 39$
quarters $2x - 12 = 2(39) - 12 = 66$

Check:

(money value nickels)	+	(money value dimes)	+	(money value quarters)		= $21.75
5(27)	+	10(39)	+	25(66)		= 2175
135	+	390	+	1650		= 2175
					2175	= 2175
						True

Answers for (?) in Example 3.   All (?) are 65.

Example 3.   Mr. Hopkins, a purchasing agent for Angel Industries, buys 8 cars and 6 pickups for his company. The total bill is $114,000.00. If a car costs $600.00 more than a pickup, what did Mr. Hopkins pay for each car and each pickup?

Let x = cost of a truck: total dollar value $6x$
Let x + 600 = cost of a car: total dollar value $8(x + 600)$

(total dollar value of cars) + (total dollar value of trucks)= 114,000

Write the equation: $8(x + 600) + 6x = 114,000$
Solve the equation: $8(x + 600) + 6x = 114,000$
$$8x + 4800 + 6x = 114,000$$
$$14x + 4800 = 114,000$$
$$14x + 4800 + (?) = 114,000 + (?)$$
$$14x = 109,200$$
$$^{14x}/_{(?)} = {}^{109200}/_{(?)}$$
$$x = 7800$$

Answer the question:

Cost of a truck is x and x = 7800
Cost of a car is x + 600 and 7800 + 600 = 8400

Check:
(total dollar value of cars) +		(total dollar value of trucks	= 114,000
8(8400)	+	6(7800)	= 114,000
$67,200	+	$46,800	=$114,000
		114,000	= 114,000
			True

Answers for (?) in Example 4.   (-4800) , 14

Exercise Set 3.3

Set up an algebraic equation that can be used to solve each problem. Solve the equation, and find the values desired.

1) When twice an unknown number is added to thirteen, the sum is 25.

2) When seven is added to an unknown number, the result is twice that unknown number.

3) When three times an unknown number is subtracted from twenty, the result is the unknown number.

4) The sum of three consecutive integers is 66. Find the numbers.

5) The sum of four consecutive odd integers is 56. Find the numbers.

6) The sum of four consecutive integers is 1 more than the third, Find them.

7) Robert Polito has $4.80 in quarters and dimes. He has a total of 30 coins. How many quarters and how many dimes does he have?

8) Ray Tiede is the purchasing agent for the Rochester Americans Hockey Team. He purchased 27 pairs of skates and 13 jerseys. The total bill was $4700. If a pair of skates cost 3 times as much as a Jersey, how much did Ray pay for each pair of skates and each jersey?

Answers for Exercise Set 3.3

1) 6	2) 7
3) 5	4) 21, 22, 23
5) 11, 13, 15, 17	6) -1, 0, 1, 2
7) 12 quarters, 18 dimes	8) jerseys: $50 each
	skates: $150 each

Section 3.4 Geometric Problems

Example 1.   The length of a rectangle is 5 less than 4 times the width.
              If the perimeter is 80, find the dimensions of the rectangle.

Let x = width
Let 4x - 5 = length

$$2L + 2W \quad = P$$

Write the equaation: $2(4x - 5) + 2x = 80$
Solve the equation: $2(4x - 5) + 2x = 80$
$$8x - 10 + 2x = 80$$
$$(?)x - 10 \quad = 80$$
$$10x - 10 + 10 = 80 + 10$$
$$10x \quad = (?)$$
$$x \quad = {}^{(?)}/_{10}$$
$$x \quad = 9$$

Answer the question: width x = 9
                    length 4x - 5 = 4(9) - 5 = 31

Check: P = 2L + 2W
          80 = 2(31) + 2(9)
          80 = 62 + 18
          80 = 80 *True*

Answers to (?) in Example 2.   10, 90

Example 2. The sum of the angles of a triangle measures 180 degrees.
If the largest angle is 90 degrees and the second angle is twice the
smallest angle, find the three unknown angles of the triangle.

Let x = the smallest angle
Let 2x = the middle angle
Let 90 = the largest angle

Write the equation: x + 2x + 90 = 180

Solve the equation:

$$
\begin{aligned}
x + 2x + 90 &= 180 \\
3x + 90 &= 180 \\
3x + 90 - 90 &= 180 - 90 \\
3x &= 90 \\
x &= {}^{90}\!/_3 \\
x &= 30
\end{aligned}
$$

Answers: smallest angle is x and x = 30
middle angle is 2x = 2(30) = 60
largest angle is 90

Check: The sum of the three angles is 30 + 60 + 90 = 180

Example 3 In a parallelogram the opposite angles have the same measures.
If the two larger angles in a parallelogram are each 45 degrees less
than two times the smaller angles, find the measures of each angle.

Let x = the measure of each of the two smaller angles
Let 2x - 45 = the measure of each of the two larger angles

Write the equation: x + x + (2x - 45) + (2x - 45) = 360

Solve the equation:

$$
\begin{aligned}
x + x + (2x - 45) + (2x - 45) &= 360 \\
6x - 90 &= 360 \\
6x - 90 + 90 &= 360 + 90 \\
6x &= 450 \\
x &= {}^{450}\!/_6 \\
x &= 75
\end{aligned}
$$

Answers: The two smaller angles   x = 75
The two larger angles 2x- 45 + 2(75) - 45 + 105

Check: The sum of all angles 75 + 75 + 105 + 105 = 360

Exercise Set 3.4

Set up an algebraic equation that can be used to solve each problem.
Solve the equation, and find the values desired.

1) The first side of a triangle is 5 less than the second side, and the
third side is twice as long as the first side. If the perimeter of the
triangle is 33, find the lengths of the side of the triangle.

2) The length of a rectangle is 2.5 times the width. If the perimeter of the rectangle is 35, find the length and width.

3) The perimeter of John Carluzzo's garden is 128 meters. If the length is three times the width, find the dimensions of the garden.

4) If the length of Ray Smith's house is twice the width and the perimeter is 1250 feet, find the dimensions of the house.

5) The measures of two angles of a triangle are the same. The third angle has a meausre that is 20 degrees more than twice the measure of either of the other two angles. How many degrees are in each angle of the triangle?

6) One angle of a triangle is 22 degrees larger than the smallest angle. The third angle is 41 degrees larger than the smallest angle. Find the number of degrees in each angle of the triangle.

7) Two angles are complementary angles if the sum of their measures is 90 degrees. If angle A and angle B are complementary angles, and angle A is eight times angle B, find the measures of angle A and angle B. Complementary angles are discussed in Appendix C. of your text.

8) The area of a triangle is 24 square centimeters and the base measures 6 centimeters. Find the number of centimeters in the measure of the altitude to that base.

9) Two angles are supplementary angles if the sum of their measures is 180 degrees. If angle A and angle B are supplementary angles, and angle A is 30 degrees less than five times angle A, find the measures of angle A and angle B. Supplementary angles are discussed in Appendix C. of your text.

10) If the two smaller angles of a parallelogram have equal measures and the two larger angles are each 50 degrees larger than a smaller angle, find the measure of each angle.

Answers for Exercise Set 3.4

1) 7, 12, 14	2) 5, 12.5
3) 16, 48	4) 208.33, 416.67
5) 40, 40, 100	6) 39, 61, 80
7) 10, 80	8) 8
9) 35, 145	10) 65, 65, 115, 115

Practice Test Chapter 3

1) Find V if V = LWH and L = 10, W = 2, H = 3.2.
2) Find H if V = $^1/_3$ BH, B = 240 and V = 960.

Solve for the variable indicated

3) L = a + (n-l)d, solve for d

4) p = 2a + b, solve for a

Set up an equation that can be used to solve each problem.
Solve the equation, and find the values desired.

5) Find two consecutive integers whose sum is 73.

6) Gordon Neal goes for a walk at a speed of 3 miles per hour. Two hours later Mark Neal attempts to overtake him by jogging at a rate of 7 miles per hour. How long will it take him to reach Gordon?

7) The first side of a triangle is 5 centimeters less than the second side, and the third side is twice as long as the first side. If the perimeter is 33 centimeters find the lengths of the sides of the triangle.

8) A man has three gallons of anti-freeze which tests 50% alcohol. How many gallons of water must be added to obtain a solution which is 30% alcohol?

9) Rick Monheim invested $4,200 in savings accounts which paid 4% and 5% interest per year. If the interest for the year was $201, how much was invested at each rate?

10) The Stitch and Thread Store buys 8 bolts of a blended wool material and 15 bolts of a cotton material for a total of $1925. A bolt of the blended wool material costs $25 more than a bolt of the cotton material. What is the cost of a bolt of the blended wool?

Answers for Practice Test Chapter 3

1) 64	2) 12
3) $d = {}^{(L-a)}/_{(n-1)}$	4) $a = {}^{(p-b)}/_{2}$
5) 36, 37	6) 1.5 hours
7) 7, 12, 14	8) 2 gallons of water
9) $ 900 at 4%	10) $100
$3300 at 5%	

Chapter 4 Exponents and Polynomials

Section 4.1 Exponents

Summary:

> In the expression x^n, **x** is referred to as the base and n is called the exponent. x^n is read "x to the nth power."
>
> $$x^n = x \cdot x \cdot x \ldots x$$
> n factors of x

Summary:

> **RULES OF EXPONENTS**
> Product Rule
> $$x^m \cdot x^n = x^{m+n}$$

Example 1. $x^7 \cdot x^2$

Solution: **Method 1**

$$x^7 \quad \cdot \quad x^2$$

$$x \cdot x \cdot x \cdot x \cdot x \cdot x \cdot x \cdot x \cdot x = x^9$$

Method 2 (Using the Product Rule)

$$x^7 \cdot x^2 = x^{7+2} = x^9$$

Example 2. Multiply using the product rule
a) $x^5 \cdot x^2$
b) $10^7 \cdot 10^5$
c) $x \cdot x^6$
d) $x^3 \cdot y^2$

Solution:
a) $x^5 \cdot x^2 = x^{5+2} = x^{(?)}$
b) $10^7 \cdot 10^5 = 10^{(?)+(?)} = 10^{12}$
c) $x \cdot x^6 = x^{(?)+(?)} = x^{(?)}$
d) $x^3 \cdot y^2 = x^3 \cdot y^2$ bases are not the same
                                                 hence do not add the exponents

Answers for (?) in Example 2.
         a) 7   b) 7 , 5   c) 1 , 6 , 7

$$\boxed{\begin{array}{c} \textbf{QUOTIENT RULE} \\ x^m/x^n = x^{m-n} \quad x \neq 0 \end{array}}$$

Example 3. Divide $x^7 \div x^4$

Solution: Method 1

$$x^7/x^4 = {}^{(x \cdot x \cdot x \cdot x \cdot x \cdot x \cdot x)}/_{(x \cdot x \cdot x \cdot x)} = {}^{1}x^3/_1 = x^3$$

Method 2 (Using the Quotient Rule)

$$x^7/x^4 = x^{7-4} = x^3$$

Example 4. Divide each expression using the quotient rule.

a) x^6/x^2 b) y^3/y c) $10^7/10^3$ d) x^5/y^2

Solution: a) $x^6/x^2 = x^{6-2} = x^4$
b) $y^3/y = y^{(?)-(?)} = y^2$
c) $10^7/10^2 = 10^{(?)-(?)} = 10^{(?)}$
d) x^5/y^2 Bases are not the same hence,
do not subtract the exponents.

Answers for (?) in Example 4.   b) 3 , 1   c) 7 , 2 , 5

$$\boxed{\begin{array}{c} \textbf{POWER RULE} \\ (x^m)^n = x^{m \cdot n} \end{array}}$$

Example 5. Simplify $(x^3)^4$

Solution: Method 1 $(x^3)^4 = (x^3)(x^3)(x^3)(x^3) = x^{3+3+3+3} = x^{12}$

Method 2 (Using Power Rule) $(x^3)^4 = x^{3 \cdot 4} = x^{12}$

Example 6. Simplify each term using the power rule.
a) $(x^5)^4$ b) $(x)^4$ c) $(10^6)^2$ d) $(y^4)^2$

Solution: a) $(x^5)^4 = x^{5 \cdot 4} = x^{20}$
b) $(x)^4 = x^{(?) \cdot 4} = x^4$
c) $(10^6)^2 = 10^{(?) \cdot (?)} = 10^{(?)}$
d) $(y^4)^2 = y^{(?) \cdot (?)} = y^{(?)}$

Answers for (?) in Example 6.   b) 1   c) 6 , 2 , 12   d) 4 , 2 , 8

ZERO EXPONENT RULE
$x^0 = 1 \quad x \neq 0$

Example 7. Simplify each expression using the zero exponent rule.

a) 25^0 b) $5x^0$ c) $(x^2)^0$ d) $(^3/_4)^0$

Solution: a) $25^0 = 1$
              b) $5x^0 = 5(x^0) = 5 \cdot (?) = 5$
              c) $(x^2)^0 = x^{2 \cdot 0} = x^0 = (?)$
              d) $(^3/_4)^0 = 1$

Answers for (?) in Example 7.   b) 1   c) 1

EXPANDED POWER RULE
$(^{ax}/_{by})^m = {}^{a^m x^m}/_{y^m}, \quad y \neq 0$

Example 8. Simplify each expression.
Write your answer without negative exponents.

a) $(2x)^3$
b) $(^{3ab}/_{9c})^2$

Solution: a) $(2x)^3 = 2^3 x^3 = 8x^3$
              b) $(^{3ab}/_{9c})^2 = {}^{3^2 a^2 b^2}/_{9^2 c^2} = {}^{9a^2 b^2}/_{81c^2}$

SUMMARY OF RULES OF EXPONENTS

1) $x^m \cdot x^n = x^{m \cdot n}$ product rule

2) $^{x^m}/_{x^n} = x^{m-n}, x \neq 0$ quotient rule

3) $(x^m)^n = x^{m \cdot n}$ power rule

4) $x^0 = 1, x \neq 0$ zero exponent rule

5) $x^{-m} = {}^1/_{x^m}, x \neq 0$ negative exponent rule

6) $(^{ax}/_y)^m = {}^{a^m x^m}/_{y^m}, y \neq 0$ expanded power rule

---

Exercise Set 4.1

Simplify each of the following.
     1) $n^2 \cdot n^5$ 2) $2^2 \cdot 2^3$
     3) $(-2)^2(-2)^5$ 4) $z^{10} \cdot z^3$

5) r^4/r^3 6) m^5/m^2

7) $15^4/15$ 8) x^{15}/x^7

9) $(2^4)^3$ 10) $(x^6)^5$

11) $(3z^2)^2$ 12) $(-5x)^2$

13) $(-0.3)^0$ 14) $(-7y)^0$

15) $-7y^0$ 16) 753^0

17) $(x^2/t)^3$ 18) $(a^4/b^3)^4$

19) $(3c/2y^2)^4$ 20) $(5m/3z^3)^4$

Answers for Exercise Set 4.1

1) n^7 2) 2^5

3) $(-2)^7$ 4) z^{13}

5) r 6) m^3

7) 15^3 8) x^8

9) 2^{12} 10) x^{30}

11) $9z^4$ 12) $25x^2$

13) 1 14) 1

15) -7 16) 1

17) x^6/t^3 18) a^{16}/b^{12}

19) $81c^4/16y^8$ 20) $25m^2/9z^6$

Section 4.2 Negative Exponents (Optional)

> **Negative Exponent Rule**
> $x^{-m} = 1/x^m$ $x \neq 0$

Example 1. Use the negative exponent rule to write each expression with positive exponents.

     a) x^{-5} b) y^{-4} c) 4^{-1} d) $1/x^{-4}$

Solution: a) $x^{-5} = 1/x^5$

                     b) $y^{-4} = 1/y^{(?)}$

                     c) $4^{-1} = {}^{(?)}/4^1 = 1/4$

                     d) $1/x^{-4} = 1/1/x^4 = 1 \div 1/x^4 = 1 \cdot x^4/1 = 1x^4/1 = x^4$

Answers for (?) in Example 1.   b) 4   c) 1

Example 2. Simplify each term. Write each answer without negative exponents.

     a) $(a^{-2})^3$ b) $(z^3)^{-2}$ c) $(n^4)^{-1}$

Solution: a) $(a^{-2})^3 = a^{(-2) \cdot (3)}$ using the power rule

                           $= a^{-6}$

                           $= 1/a^{(?)}$ using the negative exponent rule

b) $(z^3)^{-2} = z^{(3) \cdot (-2)}$ using the power rule

         $= z^{(?)}$

         $= {}^1/_{z^{(?)}}$ using the negative exponent rule

c) $(n^4)^{-1} = n^{(4)\,(-1)}$ using the power rule

         $= n^{(?)}$

         $= {}^1/_{n^{(?)}}$ using the negative exponent rule

Answers for (?) in Example 2.

     a) 6   b) -6 , 6   c) -4 , 4

Example 3.   Simplify each of the following.
Write each answer without negative exponents.

     a) ${}^{x^3}/_{x^5}$ b) ${}^{3^{-5}}/_{3^{-3}}$ c) $5x^2(3x^{-7})$ d) ${}^{10xy}/_{5x^2y^4}$

Solutions: a) ${}^{x^3}/_{x^5} = x^{3-5}$ using the quotient rule

         $= x^{-2}$

         $= {}^1/_{x^2}$ using the negative exponent rule

   b) ${}^{(3^{-5})}/_{(3^{-3})} = 3^{[-5-(-3)]}$ using the quotient rule

         $= 3^{(-5+3)}$

         $= 3^{-2}$

         $= {}^1/_{3^2}$ using the negative exponent rule

         $= {}^1/_9$

   c) $5x^2(3x^{-7}) = 5 \cdot 3 \cdot x^2 \cdot x^{-7}$

         $= 15x^{[2+(-7)]}$ using the product rule

         $= 15x^{-5}$

         $= 15(x^{-5})$

         $= 15({}^1/_{x^5})$ using the negative exponent rule

         $= {}^{15}/_{x^5}$

   d) ${}^{10xy}/_{5x^2y^4} = {}^{10x^{(1-2)}y^{(1-4)}}/_5$ using the quotient rule

         $= 2x^{-1}y^{-3}$

         $= 2(x^{-1})(y^{-3})$

         $= 2({}^1/_x)({}^1/_{y^3})$ using the negative exponent rule

         $= {}^2/_{xy^3}$

Excercise Set 4.2

Simplify each of the following. Write the answer without negative exponents.

     1) w^{-6} 2) ${}^1/_{2^{-3}}$

     3) $(2m)^{-3}$ 4) $(3a)^{-3}$

     5) ${}^{a^{-2}b^4}/_{3a^{-3}}$ 6) ${}^{28x^{-2}}/_{7y^{-3}}$

     7) ${}^{m^3}/_{n^{-2}}$ 8) ${}^{3x^{-4}}/_{15y}$

     9) $(2x^2y)(5x^{-2}y^3)$ 10) $(2r^{-4}s^2)^{-3}$

Answers for Exercise Set 4.2

1) $^1/_{w^6}$

2) 2^3

3) $^1/_{8m^3}$

4) $^1/_{27a^3}$

5) $^{ab^4}/_3$

6) $^{4y^3}/_{x^2}$

7) m^3n^2

8) $^1/_{5x^4y}$

9) $10y^4$

10) $^{r^{12}}/_{8s^6}$

Section 4.3 Scientific Notation (Optional)

Summary:

TO WRITE A NUMBER IN SCIENTIFIC NOTATION

1) Move the decimal in the original number to the right or left until you obtain a number greater than or equal to 1 and less than 10.
2) Count the number of places you have moved the decimal to obtain the number in step 1. If the decimal was moved to the left, the count is to be considered positive. If the decimal was moved to the right, the count is to be considered negative.
3) Multiply the number obtained in step 1 by 10 raised to the count (power) found in step 2.

Example 1.   Write the following numbers using scientific notation.

a) 65,879
b) 0.0093
c) 827,000
d) 70,000,000,000

Solutions:

a) 65,879   means   65,879.
   65,879.   = 6.5879×10^4

b) 0.0093   = 9.3×10^{-3}

c) 827,000   means   827,000.
   827,000.   = 8.27×10^5

d) 70,000,000,000   means   70,000,000,000.
   70,000,000,000   = 7.0×10^{10}

Summary:

> ### To Convert from a Number Given in Scientific Notion
>
> 1) Observe the exponent of the power of 10.
> 2) (a) If the exponent is positive, move the decimal in the number (greater than or equal to 1 and less than 10) to the right the same number of places as the exponent. It may be necessary to add zeros to the number.
> (b) If the exponent is negative, move the decimal in the number to the left the same number of places as the exponent. It may be necessary to add zeros.

Example 2. Write each number without exponents.

  a) 4.2×10^3 b) 3.02×10^{-5}
  c) 4.321×10^4 d) 4.002×10^{-7}

Solutions: a) $4.2 \times 10^3 = 4{,}200$
  b) $3.02 \times 10^{-5} = 0.0000302$
  c) $4.321 \times 10^4 = 43{,}210$
  d) $4.002 \times 10^{-7} = 0.0000004002$

Example 3. Multiply $(5.1 \times 10^5)(4 \times 10^{-3})$

Solution:
$$(5.1 \times 10^5)(4 \times 10^{-3}) = (5.1 \times 4)(10^5 \times 10^{-3})$$
$$= 20.4 \times 10^{5+(-3)}$$
$$= 20.4 \times 10^2$$
$$= 2040$$

Example 4. Divide $\frac{6 \times 10^{-6}}{4 \times 10^{-2}}$

Solution:
$$\frac{6 \times 10^{-6}}{4 \times 10^{-2}} = \frac{6}{4} \times \frac{10^{-6}}{10^{-2}}$$
$$= 1.5 \times 10^{-6-(-2)}$$
$$= 1.5 \times 10^{-6+2}$$
$$= 1.5 \times 10^{-4}$$
$$= 0.00015$$

Example 5. Evaluate $\frac{0.0231 \times 1200}{0.000462}$

Solution:
$$\frac{0.0231 \times 1200}{0.000462} = \frac{(2.31 \times 10^{-2})(1.2 \times 10^3)}{4.62 \times 10^{-4}}$$
$$= \frac{2.31 \times 1.2 \times 10^{-2} \times 10^{-3}}{4.62 \times 10^{-4}}$$
$$= \frac{2.772 \times 10^{-2} \times 10^3}{4.62 \times 10^{-4}}$$
$$= \frac{2.772 \times 10^{-2+3}}{4.62 \times 10^{-4}}$$
$$= \frac{2.772 \times 10}{4.62 \times 10^{-4}}$$
$$= \frac{2.772}{4.62} \times \frac{10^1}{10^{-4}}$$
$$= 0.6 \times 10^{1-(-4)}$$

$$= 0.6 \times 10^{1+4}$$
$$= 0.6 \times 10^5$$
$$= 60,000$$

Exercise Set 4.3

Express each number in scientific notation.

1) 75,000   2) 186,000
3) 0.047   4) 0.000053
5) 0.5   6) 2,320,000

Express each number without exponents.

7) 6.5×10^5 8) 2.1×10^{-2}
9) 7×10^6 10) 8.2×10^2
11) 4.002×10^{-7} 12) 4.002×10^7

Perform the indicated operation and express each number without exponents.

13) $(4.5 \times 10^3)(2.0 \times 10^4)$ 14) $\frac{6 \times 10^4}{2 \times 10^2}$
15) $(4 \times 10^{-2})(3 \times 10^5)$ 16) $\frac{4 \times 10^{-6}}{8 \times 10^{-3}}$
17) $(5 \times 10^{-7})(2 \times 10^4)$ 18) $\frac{2.5 \times 10^{-7}}{5 \times 10^{-6}}$

Perform the indicated operation by first converting each number to scientific notation form. Write the answer in scientific notation form.

19) $\frac{0.8 \times 0.0088}{0.00022}$ 20) $\frac{51,400 \times 30,900}{3,240}$

Answers for Exercise Set 4.3

1) 7.5×10^4 2) 1.86×10^5
3) 4.7×10^{-2} 4) 5.3×10^{-5}
5) 5.0×10^{-1} 6) 2.32×10^6
7) 650,000   8) 0.021
9) 7,000,000   10) 820
11) 0.0000004002   12) 40,020,000
13) 90,000,000   14) 300
15) 12,000   16) 0.0005
17) 0.01   18) 0.05
19) 3.2×10^1 20) 4.902037×10^5

Section 4.4 Addition and Subtraction of Polynomials

Summary:

A **polynomial in x** is an expression containing the sum of a finite number of terms of the form ax^n, for any real number **a** and any whole number **n**.

Examples of polynomials	*Not polynomials*	
$2x$	$4x^{1/2}$	(fractional exponent)
$\frac{1}{3}x - 4$	$3x^2 + 4x^{-1} + 5$	(negative exponent)
$x^2 - 2x + 1$	$4 + \frac{1}{x}$ $\frac{1}{x} = x^{-1}$	(negative exponent)

A polynomial is written in **descending order** (or **descending powers**) of the variable when the exponents on the variable decrease from left to right.

Example of polynomials in descending order

$$2x^3 + 4x^2 - 6x + 3$$

A **Monomial** is a one term polynomial.
A **Binomial** is a two term polynomial.
A **Trinomial** is a three term polynomial.

The degree of a term of a polynomial in one variable is the exponent of the variable.

The degree of a polynomial in one variable is the same as that of its highest degree term.

Like Terms are terms that may differ only in their numerical coefficients.

Like Terms	*Unlike Terms*
$3x$, $-4x$	$3x$, $2y$ (variables differ)
$4y$, $6y$	$2x$, $3xy$ (variables differ)
$5x^2$, $-7x^2$	$5x^2$, $5x$ (variables differ)

To add polynomials, combine the like terms of the polynomial.

Example 1.   Simplify $(3x^2 - 2x + 5) + (5x^2 + 3x - 4)$

Solution: $(3x^2 - 2x + 5) + (5x^2 + 3x - 4)$

$= 3x^2 - 2x + 5 + 5x^2 + 3x - 4$ remove parentheses

$= 3x^2 + 5x^2 - 2x + 3x + 5 - 4$ commutative property

$= (3 + 5)x^2 + (-2 + 3)x + (5 - 4)$ distributive property

$= \quad 8x^2 + x + 1$ add the coefficients

To Add Polynomials in Columns

1) Arrange polynomials in descending order one under the other with like terms in the same columns.
2) Find the sum of the terms in each column.

Example 2.   Add $(3x^2 - 2x + 5) + (5x^2 + 3x - 4)$ using columns

Solution:

$$\begin{array}{r} 3x^2 - 2x + 5 \\ + \ 5x^2 + 3x - 4 \\ \hline 8x^2 + \ x + 1 \end{array}$$

To Subtract a Polynomial add its inverse,
$a - b = a + (-b)$

1) Remove parentheses. (This will have the effect of changing the sign of **every** term within the parentheses of the polynomial being subtracted)
2) Combine like terms.

Example 3.   Simplify $(3x^2 - 2x + 7) - (2x^2 - 7x + 4)$

Solution: $(3x^2 - 2x + 7) - (2x^2 - 7x + 4)$

$= (3x^2 - 2x + 7) + (-2x^2 + 7x - 4)$

$= 3x^2 - 2x + 7 - 2x^2 + 7x - 4$ remove the parentheses

$= 3x^2 - 2x^2 - 2x + 7x + 7 - 4$ commutative property

$= (3 - 2)x^2 + (-2 + 7)x + (7 - 4)$ distributive property

$= \quad x^2 \quad + \quad 5x \quad + \quad 3$ add the coefficients

> ### TO SUBTRACT A POLYNOMIAL IN COLUMNS ADD ITS INVERSE,
> ### a - b = a + (-b)
>
> 1) Write **the polynomial being subtracted** below the polynomial from which it is being subtracted. List like terms in the same column.
> 2) Change the sign of each term in the polynomial from which it is being subtracted. (This step can be done mentally, if you like)
> 3) Find the sum of the terms in each column.

Example 4. Subtract $(2x^2 - 7x + 4)$ from $(3x^2 - 2x + 7)$

Solution:
$$3x^2 - 2x + 7$$
$$\underline{2x^2 - 7x + 4} \qquad \text{Subtract}$$

Change all signs in the second row (step 2), then add (step 3).

$$3x^2 - 2x + 7$$
$$\underline{-2x^2 + 7x - 4}$$
$$x^2 + 5x + 3$$

Exercise Set 4.4

Indicate the expressions that are polynomials. If the polynomial has a specific name — for example, monomial or binomial — give that name.

1) $3x^2 + 5$ 2) $7x^{-1} + 13$

3) -17 4) $19x^{1/2} + 9x$

Express each polynomial in descending order. If the polynomial is already in descending order, so state. Give the degree of each polynomial.

5) $8n - 7 + 5n^2$ 6) $-17x$

7) $x + 9x^2 + 3 + x^2$ 8) $^3/_4$

Add as indicated.

9) $(2m^2 - m + 4) + (3m^2 + 5m - 5)$

10) $(5n^2 + 8n - 19) + (3n^2 - 6n + 10)$

11) $(3x^2 + 4x) + (5x^2 + 7)$

12) $(2x^3 - 4) + (4x^3 + 9)$

13) Add $(5 + 8z^2)$ and $(4 - 7z^2)$

14) Add $(2b + 7b^2 - 5)$ and $(4b^2 - 2b + 8)$

15) Add in columns:

$(14x^2y^3 - 11xy^2 + 8xy)$ and $(-9x^2y^3 + 6xy^2 - 3xy)$.

Subtract as indicated.

16) Subtract $(3x^2 + 4x - 10)$ from $(5x^2 - 3x + 7)$

17) Subtract $(-8c^2 - 9c)$ from $(11c^2 - 4c)$

18) Subtract $(-5b^2 + 4b + 18)$ from $(8b^2 - 2b + 14)$

19) Subtract in columns:

$$(7y^3 + 14y^2 - 13y) \text{ from } (-10y^3 + 6y^2 + 24y)$$

20) Subtract in columns:

$$(2b + b^2 - 9) \text{ from } (8 + 3b^2 - 7b)$$

Answers to Exercise Set 4.3

1) Binomial	2) Not a polynomial.
3) Monomial	4) Not a polynomial.
5) $5n^2 + 8n - 7$, Second degree	6) $-17x$, First degree
7) $x^3 + 9x^2 + x + 3$, Third degree	8) $^3/_4$; Degree of zero
9) $5m^2 + 4m - 1$	10) $8n^2 + 2n - 9$
11) $8x^2 + 4x + 7$	12) $6x^3 + 5$
13) $z^2 + 9$	14) $11b^2 + 3$
15) $5x^2y^3 - 5xy^2 + 5xy$	16) $2x^2 - 7x + 17$
17) $19c^2 + 5c$	18) $13b^2 - 6b - 4$
19) $-17y^3 - 8y^2 + 37y$	20) $2b^2 - 9b + 17$

Section 4.5 Multiplication of Polynomials

Summary:

> **Distributive Property**
> $$a(b + c) = ab + ac$$

Example 1.   Multiply

a) $-2(3a - 2c)$ b) $2x(3x - 1)$

c) $-2h^2(5h + 3)$ d) $-2a^3(-3a^5 + 4a^2 - a)$

Solution:

$$
\begin{aligned}
\text{a) } -2(3a - 2c) &= -2[3a + (-2c)] \\
&= (-2)(3a) + (-2)(-2c) \\
&= (?)a + (?)c
\end{aligned}
$$

$$
\begin{aligned}
\text{b) } 2x(3x - 1) &= 2x[3x + (-1)] \\
&= (2x)(3x) + (2x)(-1) \\
&= (?)x^2 + (-2x) \\
&= (?)x^2 - 2x
\end{aligned}
$$

Remember, if the variables in the terms being multiplied are the same, then add the exponents.

$$
\begin{aligned}
\text{c) } -2h^2(5h + 3) &= (-2h^2)(5h) + (-2h^2)(3) \\
&= (?)h^3 + (?)h^2 \\
&= -10h^3 - 6h^2
\end{aligned}
$$

d) $-2a^3(-3a^5 + 4a^2 - a)$

$$= -2a^3[-3a^5 + 4a^2 + (-a)]$$
$$= (-2a^3)(-3a^5) + (-2a^3)(4a^2) + (-2a^3)(-a)$$
$$= (?)a^8 + (?)a^5 + (?)a^4$$
$$= 6a^8 - 8a^5 + 2a^4$$

Answers for (?) in Example 1.

    a. (-6), 4   b. 6, 6   c. (-10), (-6)   d. 6, (-8), 2

Summary:

> **Multiply a Binomial by a Binomial** using the Distributive Property:
> $$(a + b)(c + d) = (a + b)c + (a + b)d$$
> $$= ac + bc + ad + bd$$

Example 2.   Multiply $(3x - 5)(2x + 3)$
Solution: $(3x - 5)(2x + 3)$

$$= (3x - 5)2x + (3x - 5)3$$
$$= (2x)(3x) + (2x)(-5) + (3)(3x) + 3(-5)$$
$$= 6x(?) + (?)x + 9x + (?)$$
$$= 6x^2 - 10x + 9x - 15$$
$$= 6x^2 - x - 15$$

Answers for (?) in Example 2.   2, (-10), (-15)

Summary:

> A convenient method for finding the product of two binomials is the
> FOIL **method.** Consider:
> $$(a + b)(c + d)$$
>
> F stands for **first**—multiply the first terms of each binomial together:
>
>   **F**
> $$(a + b)(c + d)$$ product **ac**
>
> O stands for **outer**—multiply the two outer terms together:
>
>   **O**
> $$(a + b)(c + d)$$ product **ad**
>
> I stands for **inner**—multiply the two inner terms together:
>
>   **I**
> $$(a + b)(c + d)$$ product **bc**
>
> L stands for **last**—multiply the last terms together:
>
>   **L**
> $$(a + b)(c + d)$$ product **bd**
>
> The answer will be the sum of the products.
> $$(a + b)(c + d) = ac + ad + bc + bd$$

Example 3.   Using the FOIL **method, multiply**
$$(3x - 5)(2x + 3)$$

Solution:

$$(3x - 5)(2x + 3)$$

$$\begin{array}{cccc} F & O & I & L \\ (3x)(2x) & + (3x)(3) & + (-5)(2x) & + (3)(-5) \\ 6x^2 & + \quad 9x & - \quad 10x & - \quad 15 \\ & 6x^2 & - \quad x & - \quad 15 \end{array}$$

Example 4.   Using the FOIL **method, multiply**
$$(2m - 3)(2m - 3)$$

Solution:

$$(2m - 3)(2m - 3)$$

$$\begin{array}{cccc} F & O & I & L \\ (2m)(2m) & + (2m)(-3) & + (-3)(2m) & + (-3)(-3) \\ 4m^2 & + (-6m) & + (-6m) & + \quad 9 \\ & 4m^2 & + (?) & + \quad 9 \end{array}$$

Answer for (?) in Example 4.   (-12m)

➡**Note:** The Foil method may be only used for multiplying two binomials.

Summary:

Special Products

Product of Sum and Difference of Two Quantities

Formula 1. $(a + b)(a - b) = a^2 - b^2$ for any **a** and **b**
Derivation using the distributive property.
$$\begin{aligned} (a + b)(a - b) &= (a + b)a + (a + b)(-b) \\ &= (a)(a) + (a)(b) + (a)(-b) + (b)(-b) \\ &= a^2 + ab + (-ab) + (-b^2) \\ &= a^2 + 0ab - b^2 \\ &= a^2 - b^2 \end{aligned}$$

Square of Binomial Formulas

Formula 2. $(a + b)^2 = (a + b)(a + b) = a^2 + 2ab + b^2$
Formula 3. $(a - b)^2 = (a - b)(a - b) = a^2 - 2ab + b^2$

Derivation using the distributive property.

$$(a + b)^2 = (a + b)(a + b) = (a + b)a + (a + b)b$$
$$= (a)(a) + (a)(b) + (a)(b) + (b)(b)$$
$$= a^2 + ab + ab + b^2$$
$$= a^2 + 2ab + b^2$$

$$(a - b)^2 = (a-b)(a-b) = (a - b)a + (a - b)(-b)$$
$$= (a)(a) + (a)(-b) + (a)(-b) + (-b)(-b)$$
$$= a^2 + (-ab) + (-ab) + b^2$$
$$= a^2 - 2ab + b^2$$

Example 5.   Using the rules for finding special products perform the following multiplications.

a) $(2m + 3)(2m - 3)$
b) $(3y - 5)^2$
c) $(z + 4)^2$

Solution:

a) $(2m + 3)(2m - 3)$ where $a = 2m$ and $b = 3$

$\mathbf{(a + b)(a - b) = a^2 - b^2}$	**Formula 1**
$= (?)^2 - (?)^2$	Substitution
$= (2m)^2 - (3)^2$	
$= 4m^2 - 9$	

b) $(3y - 5)^2 = (3y - 5)(3y - 5)$ where $a = 3y$ and $b = 5$

$\mathbf{(a - b)^2 = (a - b)(a - b) = a^2 - 2ab + b^2}$	**Formula 3**
$= (?)2 - 2(?)(?) + (?)2$	Substitution
$= (3y)^2 - 2(3y)(5) + (5)^2$	
$= 9y2 - 30y + 25$	

c) $(z + 4)^2 = (z + 4)(z + 4)$ where $a = z$ and $b = 4$

$\mathbf{(a + b)^2} \quad = \mathbf{(a + b)(a + b) = a^2 + 2ab + b^2}$	**Formula 2**
$= (?)^2 + 2(?)(?) + (?)^2$	Substitution
$= (z)^2 + 2(z)(4) + (4)^2$	
$= z^2 + 8z + 16$	

Answers for (?) in Example 5.   a) 2m, 3
b) 3y, 3y, 5, 5
c) z, z, 4, 4

Exercise Set 4.4

Multiply

1) -3(2x - 5y) 2) 5a(2a² - 3a)
3) -3x(2x² - 4) 4) -a²b(-3a³ + 2ab - b²)
5) (5y + 2)(2y - 5) 6) (3x + 5)(2x - 3)
7) (5x - 2)(2x - 5) 8) (r - 5)(r - 3)
9) (2x² - 7)(3x² - 5) 10) (-5c² + d)(3c² - d)

Multiply using the special produce formula.
11) (2m + 3)² 12) (x + 9)(x - 9)
13) (y + 10)² 14) (b - 6)²
15) (m - 7)(m + 7) 16) (3r + 2)²
17) (2z - 3)² 18) (5m - 1)²
19) (2m + 6)(2m - 6) 20) (w + 4)²

Multiply using the distributive property.
21) (x - 2y)(2x² - 3xy + y²)
22) (x + 4)(6x² - 3x + 7)

Answers for Exercise Set 4.4
1) -6x + 15y 2) 10a³ - 15a²
3) -6x3 + 12x 4) 3a⁵b - 2a³b² + a²b³
5) 10y² - 21y - 10 6) 6x² + x - 15
7) 10x² - 29x + 10 8) r² - 8r + 15
9) 6x⁴ - 31x² + 35 10) -15c⁴ + 8c²d - d²
11) 4m² + 12m + 9 12) x² - 81
13) y² + 20y + 100 14) b² - 12b + 36
15) m² - 49 16) 9r² + 12r + 4
17) 4z² - 12z + 9 18) 25m² - 10m + 1
19) 4m² - 36 20) w² + 8w + 16
21) 2x³ - 7x²y + 7xy² - 2y³ 22) 6x³ + 21x² - 5x + 28

Section 4.6 Division of Polynomials

Summary:

To **divide a polynomial by a monomial,**
divide each term of the polynomial by the monomial.

Example 1. $(6x - 9)/3$
Solution: $(6x - 9)/3 = 6x/3 - 9/3$
$= 2x - (?)$

Answer for (?) in Example 1. 3

Example 2. $\frac{(15a^3 - 9a^2 + 12a - 6)}{3a}$

$$= \frac{15a^3}{3a} - \frac{9a^2}{3a} + \frac{12a}{3a} - \frac{6}{3a}$$

$$= (?)a^2 - (?)a + (?) - \frac{(?)}{a}$$

Answers for (?) in Example 2.   5 , 3 , 4 , 2

Summary:

> **DIVIDING A POLYNOMIAL BY A BINOMIAL**
> When dividing a polynomial by a binomial
> use the long division algorithm.

Example 3. $\frac{(a^2 + 7a - 18)}{(a - 2)}$ $\frac{dividend}{divisor}$

Solution: $(a - 2)\overline{)\,a^2 + 7a - 18}$

Divide a^2 (the first term in the dividend)
by a (the first term in the divisor).

$\frac{a^2}{a} = a$ **quotient**

Place the quotient, **a**, above the like term
containing **a** in the dividend.

$(a - 2)\overline{)\,a^2 + 7a - 18}$

Next, multiply **a** by **a - 2** as you would do in long division
and place the product under like terms.

$a(a - 2) = a^2 - 2a$ **product**

$$
\begin{array}{r}
a \\
(a - 2)\overline{)\,a^2 + 7a - 18} \\
\underline{a^2\ - 2a}
\end{array}
$$
                                now subtract

When subtracting, add it inverse.
a-b = a + (-b) —change the signs.

$$
\begin{array}{r}
a \\
(a - 2)\overline{)\,a^2 + 7a - 18} \\
\underline{-a^2 + 2a}
\end{array}
$$
                                Signs changed—Now Add

Next, bring down 18:

$$
\begin{array}{r}
a \\
(a - 2)\overline{)\ a^2 + 7a - 18} \\
\underline{-a^2 + 2a} \\
9a - 18
\end{array}
$$

Next, divide $^{9a}/_a = 9$ **Quotient**

Place the quotient 9 above 18 and multiply 9 times the divisor (a - 2).

$9(a - 2) = 9a - 18$

Place the product 9a - 18 under like terms.

$$
\begin{array}{r}
a + 9 \\
(a - 2)\overline{)\ a^2 + 7a - 18} \\
\underline{-a^2 + 2a} \\
9a - 18 \\
\underline{9a - 18}
\end{array}
$$

$$
\begin{array}{r}
a + 9 \\
(a - 2)\overline{)\ a^2 + 7a - 18} \\
\underline{-a^2 + 2a} \\
9a - 18 \\
\underline{-9a + 18} \\
0
\end{array}
$$
     Signs changed

     Add

$^{(a^2 + 7a - 18)}/_{(a - 2)} = a + 9$

Check: $(a - 2)(a + 9) = a^2 + 7a - 18$

              $a^2 + 9a - 2a - 18 = a^2 + 7a - 18$

              $a^2 + 7a - 18 = a^2 + 7a - 18$ *True*

Example 4. $^{(x^2 + 8x + 15)}/_{(x + 5)}$

$$
\begin{array}{r}
x \\
(x + 5)\overline{)\ x^2 + 8x + 15} \\
\underline{-x^2 - 5x} \\
3x - 18
\end{array}
$$
     Signs changed

     Add

$$\begin{array}{r} x + 3 \\ (x+5)\overline{)\; x^2 + 8x + 15} \\ \underline{-x^2 - 5x} \\ 3x + 15 \\ \underline{-3x - 15} \\ 0 \end{array}$$ **Signs changed**
                                                Add

$$^{x^2 + 8x + 15}/_{x+5} = x + 3$$

Check: $(x+5)(x+3) = x^2 + 8x + 15$
                $x^2 + 3x + 5x + 15 = x^2 + 8x + 15$
                $x^2 + 8x + 15 = x^2 + 8x + 15$ *True*

Exercise Set 4.6

Divide as indicated.

1) $^{(24a^2 - 12a)}/_{-6}$ 2) $^{(4 + 8x)}/_4$

3) $^{6x - 8y}/_2$ 4) $^{(3x + 6)}/_3$

5) $^{(10x + 15)}/_5$ 6) $^{(4y^2 - 3y)}/_y$

7) $^{(13a - a^2b^2 + a^2b)}/_{a^2b}$ 8) $^{(12x^3 - 8x^2 + 3x)}/_{4x}$

9) $^{(5x^3 - 4x^2 + 10)}/_{-5x^2}$ 10) $^{(-15a^4 + 12a^3 - 18a^2)}/_{-3a^2}$

11) $^{(x^2 + 5x + 6)}/_{(x+2)}$ 12) $^{(x^2 + 5y + 6)}/_{(x+3)}$

13) $^{(x^2 - 9x + 20)}/_{(x-4)}$ 14) $^{(x^2 - x - 12)}/_{(x+3)}$

15) $^{(6x^2 + 5x - 6)}/_{(3x-2)}$ 16) $^{(20x^2 + 13x - 15)}/_{(5x-3)}$

17) $^{(15y^2 + 19y + 10)}/_{(5y-7)}$ 18) $^{(8a^2 - 2ab - b^2)}/_{(4a+b)}$

19) $^{(6a^2 + 5ab + b^2)}/_{(2a+3b)}$ 20) $^{(6a^2 + 5ab - b^2)}/_{(3a-2b)}$

Answers for Exercise Set 4.6

1) $-4a^2 + 2a$ 2) $1 + 2x$
3) $3x - 4y$ 4) $x + 2$
5) $2x + 3$ 6) $4y - 3$
7) $^{13}/_{ab} - b + 1$ 8) $3x^2 - 2x + ^3/_4$
9) $-x + ^4/_5 - ^2/_{x^2}$ 10) $5a^2 - 4a + 6$
11) $x + 3$ 12) $x + 2$
13) $x - 5$ 14) $x - 4$
15) $2x + 3$ 16) $4x + 5$
17) $3y + 8 + ^{66}/_{(5y-7)}$ 18) $2a - b$
19) $3a - 2b + ^{7b^2}/_{(2a+3b)}$ 20) $2a + 3b + ^{7b^2}/_{(3a-2b)}$

Section 4.7 Rate and Mixture Problems

Summary:

```
┌─────────────────────────────┐
│      Rate Problems          │
│                             │
│   amount = rate • time      │
└─────────────────────────────┘
```

Example 1. A swimming pool is being filled, by the parks department, at a rate of 15 gallons per minute. If the pool requires 7,350 gallons of water, how long will it take to fill the pool?

Solution:

$$
\begin{aligned}
\text{Let } x &= \text{time in minutes} \\
\text{amount} &= \text{rate} \cdot \text{time} \\
7{,}350 &= 15 \cdot x \\
\tfrac{7{,}350}{15} &= x \\
490 \text{ minutes} &= x
\end{aligned}
$$

Example 2. It took a highway construction crew 8 weeks to build a 96 mile stretch of highway in Wayne County. Find the rate of highway completed per week.

Solution:

$$
\begin{aligned}
\text{Let } x &= \text{rate per week} \\
\text{amount} &= \text{rate} \cdot \text{time} \\
96 &= x \cdot 8 \\
\tfrac{96}{8} &= x \\
12 &= x
\end{aligned}
$$

12 miles per week

Example 3. Two friends, 10 miles apart, decided to meet at a point between them. One person walks for $3/4$ hour to reach, the point. The other person rides a bike for $1/2$ hour to reach the point. The constant rate for the rider is 10 miles per hour faster than that of the walker. What is the constant speed for each? How far does each travel to reach the point?

Solution: Let x = rate of the walker
Let x + 10 = rate of the rider

	rate •	time	=	distance (amount)
walker	x	$3/4$		$3/4 x$
rider	x + 10	$1/2$		$1/2 (x + 10)$

distance of walker	+	distance of rider	=	10
$^3/_4x$	+	$^1/_2(x+10)$	=	10
$^3/_4x$	+	$^1/_2 x + 5$	=	10
$4 \cdot {}^3/_4x$	+	$4 \cdot ({}^1/_2 x + 5)$	=	$4 \cdot (10)$
$^{12}/_4x$	+	$^4/_2 x + 20$	=	40
$3x$	+	$2x + 20$	=	40
		$5x + 20$	=	40
		$5x + 20 + (?)$	=	$40 + (?)$
		$5x$	=	20
		x	=	$^{20}/_{(?)}$
		x	=	4

walkers rate is $x = 4$ mph
riders rate is $x + 10 = 4 + 10 = 14$ mph
Distance traveled by the walker is $^3/_4x = ^3/_4 \cdot 4 = 3$ miles
Distance traveled by the rider is $^1/_2(x + 10) = ^1/_2(4 + 10) = 7$ miles

Answers or (?) in Example 3.   (-20) , 5

Example 4.   The car travels from Rochester, N.Y. to Buffalo, N.Y. at 50 miles per hour. A second car leaves Rochester for Buffalo on the same highway 45 minutes later at 80 miles per hour. How long will it take the second car to overtake the first car?

Solution: Let x = travel time in hours for the first car from Rochester to Buffalo

Since the units of measure are miles per hour 45 minutes should be changed to hours.

45 minutes = $^3/_4$ hour

Let $x - ^3/_4$ = travel time for the second car from Rochester to Buffalo.

rate	•	time	=	distance
1st car	50	x		$50x$
2nd car	80	$x - ^3/_4$		$80(x - ^3/_4)$

distance of 1st car	=	distance of 2nd car
$50x$	=	$80(x - ^3/_4)$
$50x$	=	$80x - 60$
$50x + (?)$	=	$80x + (?) - 60$
$-30x$	=	-60
x	=	$^{-60}/_{(?)}$
x	=	2

In 2 hours the second car will overtake the first car.

Answers for (?) in Example 4. (-80x), -30.

Example 1. At Red Wing Stadium, game tickets were sold at $2.50, $5.00, and $8.00 each. The number sold at $5.00 was 100 more than the number sold at $8.00. The total receipts were $14,000.00. Find the number sold at each price if 200 were sold at $2.50.

Solution: Let x = number of $8.00 seats sold.
Let x + 100 = number of $5.00 seats sold.

	price	No. of tickets	Total Cost
$2.50 seat	2.50	200	2.50 (200)
$5.00 seat	5.00	x + 100	5 (x + 100)
$8.00 seat	8.00	x	8x

Cost of $2.50 seats + Cost of $5.00 seats + Cost of $8.00 seats   = $14,000
$$2.50 \ (200) \quad + \quad 5 \ (x + 100) \quad + \quad 8x \qquad = 14,000$$
$$500 \quad + \quad 5 \ x + 500 \quad + \quad 8x \qquad = 14,000$$
$$13x + 1000 \qquad = 14,000$$
$$13x + 1000 + (?) \qquad = 14,000 + (?)$$
$$13x \qquad = 13,000$$
$$^{13x}/_{(?)} \qquad = {}^{13,000}/_{(?)}$$
$$x \qquad = 1,000$$

200 tickets at $2.50 each   200 x 2.50 =   500
1,100 tickets at $5.00 each   1,100 x 5.00 = 5,500
1,000 tickets at $8.00 each   1,000 x 8.00 = <u>8,000</u>
14,000

Answer for (?) in Example 1.   (-1,000) , 13

Example 2. Juan Valdez, a coffee merchant from Columbia, blends coffee worth 75 cents a pound with coffee worth 95 cents a pound. How many pounds of each grade did he use to make a mixture of 30 pounds valued at 85 cents a pound?

Solution:

Let x = number of pounds of coffee at 75 cents

Let 30 - x = number of pounds of coffee at 85 cents

	price	quantity	Total Price
75 cent blend	75	x	75x
95 cent blend	95	30 - x	95(30 - x)
mixture	85	30	85 (30)

Total Price 75 cent blend + Total Price 95 cent blend = Total Price Mixture

75x	+	95(30 - x)	= 85 (30)
75x	+	2850 - 95x	= 2550
		-20x + 2850	= 2550
		-20x + 2850 + (?)	= 2550 + (?)
		-20x	= -300
		x	= $^{-300}/_{(?)}$
		x	= 15

15 pounds of 75 cent coffee is blended with 15 pounds of 95 cent coffee to produce the new mixture.

Example 3. Chuck VonHoltz has a 70% alcohol solution and a 50% alcohol solution. How much of each could he use if he wants to obtain 25 pints of a mixture that is 55% alcohol?

Solution:

Let x = number of pints of 70% alcohol solution.

Let 25 - x = number of pints of 50% alcohol solution.

Strength of Solution	Pints of solution	Amount of Alcohol
70% = 0.70	x	.70x
50% = 0.50	25 - x	.50(25 - x)
55% = 0.55	25	.55 (25)

70% alcohol	+	50% alcohol	= Alcohol in the combined solution
0.70x	+	0.50(25 - x)	= 0.55 (25)
0.70x	+	12.5 - 0.50x	= 13.75

$$100 (0.70x + 12.5 - 0.50x) = 100(13.75)$$
$$70x + 1250 - 50x = 1375$$
$$20x + 1250 = 1375$$
$$20x + 1250 \ (?) = 1375 + (?)$$
$$20x = 125$$
$$x = {}^{125}/_{(?)}$$
$$x = 6.25$$

6.25 pints of a 70% alcohol solution plus 18.75 pints of a 50% alcohol solution will produce 25 pints of a 55% alcohol solution.

Answers for (?) in Example 3. (-1250), 20

Example 4   In a triangle, one angle is twice as large as another angle and the third angle is 40° larger than the smallest angle. Find all three angles. Recall that the sum of the interior angles of triangle is 180°.

Solution: Let x = 1st angle
$2x$ = 2nd angle
$x + 40$ = 3rd angle

$$(\text{1st angle}) + (\text{2nd angle}) + (\text{3rd angle}) = 180$$
$$x \ + \ 2x \ + \ x+40 = 180$$
$$4x + 40 = 180$$
$$4x + 40 + (?) = 180 + (?)$$
$$4x = 140$$
$$x = {}^{140}/_{(?)}$$
$$x = 35$$

Since the first angle is represented by x, the angle is 35°.
The second angle is represented by 2x, the angle is 2(35°) or 70°.
The third angle is represented by (x+40), the angle is (35+40) or 75°.
Check 35° + 70° + 75° = 180°.

Answer for (?) in Example 4.   (-40), 4

Exercise Set 4.7

1) A cruise missile travels at a rate of 600 mph. If the target is 300 miles away, how long will it take for the missle to reach its target?

2) John, a brick layer, can lay 36 bricks per hour. How many bricks can John lay in $^5/_6$ of an hour?

3) If it takes 2 hours to drive from Alton N.Y. to Utica, N.Y., a total of 70 miles, what is the rate of travel in miles per hour?

4) Richard Moore ran the Boston Marathon a distance of 25 miles, in 5.5 hours. Find Richard's rate per hour.

5) The Evil Eye Lure Company has a punch press that can produce fishing lures at a rate of 175 lures per hour, how many lures can be manufactured in 8 hours?

6) Two airplanes start from the same airport and travel in opposite directions. One plane travels at 550 mph and the other at 650 mph. How long will it take the two planes to be 300 miles apart?

7) Paul Riker leaves town at noon on a bicycle traveling west at a rate of 15 mph. At 4 p.m. Lisa Riker leaves town in a car traveling in the same direction at a rate of 45 mph. How many hours will it take Lisa to catch Paul?

8) Curt Smith leaves Whitney Point, N .Y., in a car traveling east at a rate of 45 mph. At the same time, Gail Smith leaves Whitney Point in a car traveling west at a rate of 55 mph. In how many hours will Curt and Gail be 360 miles apart?

9) Mike Tari leaves Sodus, N.Y. at 1 p.m. on horseback traveling south at a rate of 12 mph. At 3:30 p.m. Sharon Tari leaves Sodus by jeep traveling in the same direction at a rate of 37 mph. How many hours will it take Sharon to catch Mike?

10) A man drives from home to work in 45 minutes. After work he returns home during rush hour, at 20 mph less than his rate going to work. The total round trip time is 2 hours. a) How fast does he travel on each part of the commute? b) How far is his home from work?

11) Wo Fat, from the China Tea House, wishes to mix a tea worth $1.00 an ounce with another tea worth $.60 an ounce, how many ounces of each does he need to use if he wants 22 pounds of a mixture worth $.75 an ounce? (Note there are 16 ounces in a pound)

12) A gourmet food shop wants to mix some $2-per pound coffee beans with 30 pounds of $3-per pound coffee beans to produce a mixture which will sell for $2.60 per pound. How much $2-per pound coffee should be used?

13) Pat Nettnin invested an amount of money at an annual interest rate of 9%. She invested $2,700 more than this amount at 12% annually. The total yearly income from these investments was $1,794. How much did she invest at each rate?

14) Gib Sergeant has $5.85 in quarters and dimes. If he has 4 times as many dimes as quarters, how many dimes and how many quarters does he have?

15) Brian Neal wants to mix 20% anti-freeze solution with 45% anti-freeze solution to obtain 15 pints of a solution that is 30% anti-freeze. How much of each solution should he use in his mixture?

16) If you have a 40% alcohol solution and a 70% alcohol solution, how much of each do you need to make 21 gallons of a solution that is 50% alcohol?

17) Joe Snyder invested $4000, in two different mutual funds. One fund returned a yield of 15% last year, but the other fund only returned 5% last year. Joe made $440 on his two investments last year. How much was invested in the mutual fund?

Answers for Exercise Set 4.7

1) 0.5 hour or 30 minutes	2) 30 bricks
3) 35 mph	4) 4.5 mph (rounded)
5) 1400 lures	6) 2.5 hours
7) 2 hours	8) 3.6 hours
9) 1.5 hours	10) 50 mph; 37.5 miles

11) 15 ounces at $1.00 per ounce
    25 ounces at $ .60 per ounce

12) 20 pounds of $2-per pound coffee

13) $7000 at 9% and $9700 at 12%

14) 36 dimes, 9 quarters

15) 6 pints of 45% anti-freeze
    9 pints of 20% anti-freeze

16) 14 gallons of 40% alcohol
    7 gallons of 70% alcohol

17) $1,600 at 5% , $2,400 at 15%

Practice Test Chapter 4
Simplify, and express your answer without negative exponents.

1) $5x^5 \cdot 3x^8$

2) $(2y^2)^5$

3) $\dfrac{9y^3}{3y}$

4) $(3x^{-2}y^{-1})^{-2}$

5) $\left(\dfrac{3a^3b^4}{2ab^3}\right)^3$

6) $\dfrac{3z^6}{27z^{-4}}$

In problems 7 through 9, determine whether each expression is a polynomial.
If the polynomial has a specific name, give the name.

7) $x^{-2} + 3x + 5$ 8) $x^2 + 5x$ 9) $16x$

Perform the operations indicated.

10) $(8z^2 + 5) + (z^2 + 7)$

11) $(4a^2 - 3a + 6) - (3a^2 + 5a - 4)$

12) $(8 + 3b^2 - 7b) + (2b + b^2 - 9)$

13) $-4m^3(2m^3 - 3m^2 + m - 5)$

14) $(x + 3)(x - 3)$

15) $(2x + 5)^2$

16) $(3x + 7)(4x - 6)$

17) $(x + 3x^3 + 4)(5 - x)$

18) $(2x^2 + 3x)/x$

19) $(15v^2 + 19v - 4)/(3v + 8)$

Perform the indicated operation by first converting each number to scientific notation
form. Write the answer in scientific form.

20) $(0.0000089)(38,400)$

21) $(0.000613) \div (0.0207)$

22) $93,000,000/186,000 \times 365$

Answers for Practice Test Chapter 4

1) $15x^{13}$ 2) $32y^{10}$

3) $3y^2$ 4) $x^4y^2/9$

5) $9a^6b^3/x$ 6) $z^{10}/9$

7) Not polynomial   8) Binomial

9) Monomial   10) $9z^2 + 12$

11) $a^2 - 8a + 10$ 12) $4b^2 - 5b - 1$

13) $-8m^6 + 12m^5 - 4m^4 + 20m^3$ 14) $x^2 - 9$

15) $4x^2 + 20x + 25$ 16) $12x^2 + 10x - 42$

17) $-3x^4 + 15x^3 - x^2 + x + 20$ 18) $2x + 3$

19) $5v - 7 + 52/(3v + 8)$ 20) 3.4176×10^{-1}

21) $2.9613527 \, x^{-2}$ 22) 1.369863×10^0

❖❖❖❖❖❖❖❖❖❖❖❖❖❖❖

Chapter 5 Factoring

Section 5.1 Factoring a Monomial from a Polynomial

Summary:

> To factor an expression means to write the expression as a product of its factors.
>
> **To determine the GCF of two or more numbers:**
> a) Write each number as a product of prime numbers;
> b) Determine the prime factors common to all the numbers;
> c) Multiply the common factors found in the second step. The product of these factors will be the Greatest Common Factor (**GCF**).

Example 1.   Find the GCF of 18 and 36.

Solution: $18 = 2 \cdot 3 \cdot 3 = 2 \cdot 3^2$
$36 = 2 \cdot 2 \cdot 3 . 3 = 2^2 \cdot 3^2$
$GCF = 2 \cdot 3^2 = 2 \cdot 9 = 18$

Summary:

> **Greatest Common Factor of two or more terms**
>
> To find the **GCF**, of two or more terms, take each factor the **fewest** number of times that it appears in any of the terms.

Example 2.   Find GCF of the terms: x^2 , x^5 , x , x^8

Solution: $x^2 = x \cdot x$
$x^5 = x \cdot x \cdot x \cdot x \cdot x$
$x = x$
$x^8 = x \cdot x \cdot x \cdot x \cdot x \cdot x \cdot x \cdot x$
$GCF = x$

Example 3.   Find the GCF of the terms: x^5y^2 , x^8y^3 , x^3y^7

Solution: The GCF is x^3y^2. The smallest power of **x** that appears in any of the terms is x^3 and the smallest power of **y** that appears in any of the terms is y^2.

Example 4.   Find GCF of each pair of terms:
a) $5r^3$, $10r^2$, $15r$
b) $-18s$, $-6s^2$, $-12s^3$
c.) $5m^4n$, $15m^3n^2$, $10m^2n^3$
d) $24d^5$, $60d^4$, $36d^3$, $48d^2$

Solution: a) The GCF of 5, 10, and 15 is 5.
   The GCF of r^3, r^2, and r is r.
   The GCF of the three terms is 5r.

b) The GCF of -18, -6, and -12 is -6.
   The GCF of s, s^2, and s^3 is s.
   The GCF of the three terms is -6s.

c) The GCF of 5, 15, and 10 is 5.
   The GCF of m^4, m^3, and m^2 is m^2.
   The GCF of n, n^2, and n^3 is n.
   The GCF of the three terms is $5m^2n$.

d) The GCF of 24, 60, 36, and 48 is 12.
   The GCF of d^5, d^4, d^3, and d^2 is d^2.
   The GCF of the three terms is $12d^2$.

Example 5.   Find the GCF of each pair of terms:
a) $x(x + 14)$ and $5(x + 14)$
b) $10(x + 6)$ and $30(2x + 5)$
c) $2x(y + 6)$ and $6x(y + 7)$

Solution: a) The GCF is $(x + 14)$.
b) The GCF is 10.
c) The GCF is 2x.

To Factor a Monomial from a Polynomial

1) Determine the greatest common factor of all terms in the polynomial.
2) Write each term as the product of the GCF and its other factor.
3) Use the distributive property to factor out the GCF.

Example 6.   Factor:
a) $4x - 10$ b) $12 - 3 + 6s$
c) $-15abc - 10ab$ d) $7x^2y - 14xy^2$
e) $x(2x - 5) + 4(2x - 5)$

Solution: a)   4x - 10   GCF is 2
                 4x - 10 = 2(2x - 5)   Factored

            b)   12 - 3 + 6s   GCF is 3
                 12 - 3 + 6s = 3(4 - 1 + 2s)   Factored

            c)   -15abc - 10ab   GCF is -5ab
                 -15abc - 10ab = -5ab(3c + 2)   Factored

            d) $7x^2 - 14xy^2$ GCF is 7x
                 $7x^2y - 14xy^2 = 7x(x - 2y)$ Factored

            e)   x(2x - 5) + 4(2x - 5)   GCF is (2x - 5)
                 x(2x - 5) + 4(2x - 5)
                 = (2x - 5)(x + 4)   Factored

Exercise Set 5.1

Write each number as a product of prime numbers:

    1) 60   2) 27

Find the greatest common factor for the two given numbers:

    3) 45 , 15   4) 26 , 39

Determine the greatest common factor for each set of terms:

    5) $8x^3y^5$, $4xy^2$ 6) $14x^2$, $2x$
    7) $6x^2$, $2x^3$ 8) $12a^4b^7$, $6a^3b$
    9) $15x^2y^3$, $3x^4y^2$ 10) $-28a^6b^2$, $-14a^2b^5$

Factor the GCF from each term in the expression.
If an expression cannot be factored, so state.

    11) 3a + 3b   12) 4x + 2
    13) 9t - 6   14) $14x^2 - 21x$
    15) $9y^2 - 6y$ 16) $-30m^4 + 45m^2t^2$
    17) $x^2y^3 - x^3y^2$ 18) $-8xy - 24x^2y^2$
    19) (m+n)(m+n) - (m+n)   20) a(a + b) - 5(a + b)

Answers for Exercise Set 5.1

    1) 2 • 2 • 3 • 5   2) 3 • 3 • 3
    3) 15   4) 13
    5) $4xy^2$ 6) 2x
    7) $2x^2$ 8) $6a^3b$
    9) $3x^2y^2$ 10) $-14a^2b^2$
    11) 3(a + b)   12) 2(2x + 1)
    13) 3(3t - 2)   14) 7x(2x - 3)
    15) 3y(3y - 2)   16) $15m^2(-2m^2 + 3t^2)$
    17) $x^2y^2(y - x)$ 18) -8xy(1 + 3xy)
    19) (m + 1)[(m + n) - 1]   20) (a + b)(a - 5)

Section 5.2 Factor by Grouping

To Factor a Four-term Polynomial Using Grouping

1) Determine if there are any factors common to all four terms. If so, factor the greatest common factor from each term of the four terms.

2) If necessary, arrange the four terms so that the first two terms have a common factor and the last two terms have a common factor.

3) Use the distributive property to factor each group of two terms.

4) Factor the greatest common factor from the result of step 3.

Example 1.   Factor $ax + 2t + ay + 2ty$ by grouping.

Solution: $ax + 2tx$ $+$ $ay + 2ty$
(x is common)   (y is common)

$x(a + 2t)$ $+$ $y(a + 2t)$
        [(a + 2t) is common]

$(a + 2t)(x + y)$ **Factored**

Example 2.   Factor $4m^2 + 16m + 12mx + 48x$ by grouping.

Solution: $4m^2 + 16m + 12mx + 48x$ GCF is 4
$4(m^2 + 4m + 3mx + 12x)$
$4(m^2 + 4m$ $+$ $3mx + 12x)$
(m is common)   (3x is common)

$4[m(m + 4)$ $+$ $3x(m + 4)]$
        [(m + 4) is common]

$4(m + 4)(m + 3x)$ **Factored**

Example 3.   Factor $-x^3 + bx^2 + 3b^2x - 3b^3$ by grouping.

Solution: $-x^3 + bx^2$ $+$ $3b^2x - 3b^3$
(x^2 is common)   ($-3b^2$ is common)

$x^2(-x + b)$ $-$ $3b^2(-x + b)$
        [(-x + b) is common]

$(-x + b)(x^2 - 3b^2)$ **Factored**

Exercise Set 5.2

Factor by grouping.

1) $ax - ay + bx - by$
2) $2cx + vx + 4cy + 2yv$
3) $x^2 + cx - ax - ac$
4) $x^2 - 3x + 2xy - 6y$
5) $a^3 + 2ab^2 - 4b^3 - 2a^2b$
6) $x^3 - x^2 + 7x - 7$
7) $12x - 3bx - 72y + 18by$
8) $bx^2 + x + bx + 1$
9) $36y^3 - 18y^2 - 84y + 42$
10) $18m - 12m^2 + 24m^3 - 16m^4$
11) $t^2 - 3t - 3t + 9$
12) $y^2 - y - y + 1$

Answers for Exercise Set 5.2

1) $(x - y)(a + b)$
2) $(x + 2y)(2c + v)$
3) $(x + c)(x - a)$
4) $(x - 3)(x + 2y)$
5) $(a^2 + 2b^2)(a - 2b)$
6) $(x - 1)(x^2 + 7)$
7) $3(4 - b)(x - 6y)$
8) $(bx + 1)(x + 1)$
9) $6(3y^2 - 7)(2y - 1)$
10) $2m(3 + 4m^2)(3 - 2m)$
11) $(t - 3)(t - 3)$
12) $(y - 1)(y - 1)$

Section 5.3 Factoring Trinomials with a = 1.

Summary:

> **To Factor Trinomials of the Form $ax^2 + bx + c$, where $a = 1$**
>
> 1) Determine two numbers whose product equals the constant, **c**, and whose sum equals **b**.
>
> 2) The factors of the trinomial will be:
> $(x +$ first number), and $(x +$ second number).

Example 1:   Factor $x^2 - 5x - 14$

Solution: We must find two numbers whose product is (-14) and whose sum is (-5).

Factors of (-14)	Sum of Factors
$2(7) = 14$	$2 + 7 = 9$
$(-2)(-7) = 14$	$-2 + (-7) = -9$
$-2(7) = -14$	$-2 + 7 = 5$
$2(-7) = -14$	$2 + (-7) = -5$

The factors are
$(x + 2)(x - 7)$

Check: FOIL Method to multiply two binomials:

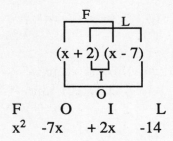

$$F \qquad O \qquad I \qquad L$$
$$x^2 \quad -7x \quad +2x \quad -14$$

➡**Note:** That the sum of the inner terms $-7x + 2x = -5x$ and the product of the last terms is $(2)(-7) = -14$.

Refer to these two ideas in trying to find factors for a given trinomial.

Example 2. Factor $x^2 + 6x + 9$.

Solution: We must find two numbers whose product is 9 and whose sum is 6.

Factors of 9	Sum of Factors
$1(9) = 9$	$1 + 9 = 10$
$3(3) = 9$	$3 + 3 = 6$
$(-1)(-9) = 9$	$(-1) + (-9) = -10$
$(-3)(-3) = 9$	$(-3) + (-3) = -6$

The factors are $(x + 3)(x + 3)$
$x^2 + 6x + 9 = (x + 3)(x + 3)$ **Factored**

Check: $x^2 + 6x + 9 = (x + 3)(x + 3)$
$x^2 + 6x + 9 = x^2 + 3x + 3x + 9$
$x^2 + 6x + 9 = x^2 + 6x + 9$ **True**

Example 3. Factor $b^2 - 9b + 14$

Solution: We must find two numbers whose product is 14 and whose sum is (-9).

Factors of 14	Sum of Factors
$1(14) = 14$	$1 + 14 = 15$
$2(7) = 14$	$2 + 7 = 9$
$(-1)(-14) = 14$	$(-1) + (-14) = -15$
$(-2)(-7) = 14$	$(-2) + (-7) = -9$

The factors are $(b - 2)(b - 7)$
$b^2 - 9b + 14 = (b - 2)(b - 7)$ **Factored**

Example 4.   Factor $t^2 + 11t - 30$.

Solution: We must find the two numbers whose product is (-30) and whose sum is 11.

Factors of (-30)	**Sum of Factors**
$1(-30) = -30$	$1 + (-30) = -29$
$2(-15) = -30$	$2 + (-15) = -13$
$3(-10) = -30$	$3 + (-10) = -7$
$5(-6) = -30$	$5 + (-6) = -1$
$(-1)(30) = -30$	$(-1) + 30 = 29$
$(-2)(15) = -30$	$(-2) + 15 = 13$
$(-3)(10) = -30$	$(-3) + 10 = 7$
$(-5)(6) = -30$	$(-5) + 6 = 1$

Since it is not possible to sum any of the pairs of factors and get 11, the trinomial cannot be factored.

Example 5.   Factor $r^2 - 13rs - 48s^2$

Solution: We must find the two numbers whose product is (-48) and whose sum is (-13).

Factors of (-48)	**Sum of Factors**
$1(-48) = -48$	$1 + (-48) = -47$
$2(-24) = -48$	$2 + (-24) = -22$
$3(-16) = -48$	**$3 + (-16) = -13$**
$4(-12) = -48$	$4 + (-12) = -8$
$6(-8) = -48$	$6 + (-8) = -2$
$8(-6) = -48$	$8 + (-6) = 2$

The factors are $(r + 3s)(r - 16s)$
$r^2 = 13rs - 48s^2 = (r + 3s)(r - 16s)$ **Factored**

Example 6.   Factor $2y^2 - 30y + 72$ completely.

Solution: Since the numerical coefficient of the squared term is not 1, check for a common factor.

$2y^2 - 30y + 72$ **GCF is 2**
$2y^2 - 30y + 72 = 2(y^2 - 15y + 36)$

Now factor $y^2 - 15y + 36$
The factors are $(y - 12)(y - 3)$

$2y^2 - 30y + 72 = 2(y - 12)(y - 3)$ **Factored**

Exercise Set 5.3

Factor each expression. If an expression cannot be factored by the method presented in this section, so state.

1) $x^2 - 8x + 12$ 2) $y^2 + 3y + 2$
3) $x^2 + 12x + 35$ 4) $x^2 - 34x - 35$
5) $m^2 - 6m + 9$ 6) $b^2 + 4b - 21$
7) $y^2 + y - 2$ 8) $m^2 + 4m + 6$
9) $b^2 + 2b - 8$ 10) $x^2 - 9xy + 20y^2$
11) $x^2 + 2x - 35$ 12) $x^2 - 9xy + 20y^2$
13) $c^2 + cx - 56x^2$ 14) $b^2 - 15bz + 36z^2$

Factor Completely:

15) $2y^2 + 6y - 20$ 16) $-4t^2 + 12t - 8$
17) $2m^2 + 6m - 36$ 18) $3y^2 + 12y + 12$
19) $-4z^4 + 52z^3 - 168z^2$ 20) $-3y^3 + 39y^2 + 144y$

Answers to Exercise Set 5.3.

1) $(x - 6)(x - 2)$ 2) $(y + 2)(y + 1)$
3) $(x + 5)(x + 7)$ 4) $(x + 1)(x - 35)$
5) $(m - 3)(m - 3)$ 6) $(b - 3)(b + 7)$
7) $(y - 1)(y + 2)$ 8) Cannot be factored.
9) $(b - 2)(b + 4)$ 10) $(x - 5y)(x - 4y)$
11) $(x - 5)(x + 7)$ 12) $(x - 4y)(x - 5y)$
13) $(c - 7x)(c + 8x)$ 14) $(b - 3z)(b - 12z)$
15) $2(y - 2)(y + 5)$ 16) $-4(t - 2)(t - 1)$
17) $2(m - 3)(m + 6)$ 18) $3(y + 2)(y + 2)$
19) $-4z^2(z - 6)(z - 7)$ 20) $-3y(y + 3)(y - 16)$

Section 5.4   Factoring Trinomials with $a \neq 1$.

Method 1

To factor Trinomials of the Form $ax^2 + bx + c$, $a \neq 1$,
Using Trial and Error

1) Determine if there is any factor common to all three terms. If so, factor it out.
2) Write all pairs of factors of the coefficient of the squared term, a.
3) Write all pairs of the factors of the constant, c.
4) Try various combinations of these factors until the correct middle term, bx, is found

Example 1   Factor $3x^2 + x - 2$

Solution:

Factors of 3	Factors of (-2)	Possible factors of Trinomial	Sum of the Products of Outer and Inner Terms
1(3)	1(-2)	$(x + 1)(3x - 2)$	1x
1(3)	-1(2)	$(x - 1)(3x + 2)$	-1x
1(3)	1(-2)	$(3x + 1)(x - 2)$	-5x
1(3)	-1(2)	$(3x - 1)(x + 2)$	5x

Since the product of $(x + 1)(3x - 2)$ yields the correct **bx** term, **1x,** they are the correct factors.

$$3x^2 + x - 2 = (x - 1)(3x + 2)$$

Example 2   Factor $3x^2 + 7x + 2$

Solution:

Factors of 3	Factors of 2	Possible factors of Trinomial	Sum of the Products of Outer and Inner Terms
1(3)	1(2)	$(x + 1)(3x + 2)$	5x
1(3)	1(2)	$(x + 2)(3x + 1)$	7x
1(3)	-1(-2)	$(x - 1)(3x - 2)$	-5x
1(3)	-1(-2)	$(x - 2)(3x - 1)$	-7x

Since the product of $(x - 2)(3x - 2)$ yields the correct **bx** term, **-7x,** they are the correct factors.

$$3x^2 - 7x + 2 = (x - 2)(3x - 1)$$

Method 2

> **To Factor Trinomials of the Form $ax^2 + bx + c$, $a \neq 1$**
>
> 1) Find two numbers whose product is equal to the product of **a** times **c**, and whose sum is equal to **b**.
> 2) Rewrite the **bx** term using the factors found in step 1.
> 3) Factor by grouping as explained in Section 5.2.

Example 1.   Factor $3x^2 + x - 2$

Solution: First determine if there is a common factor to all three terms of the polynomial. There are no common factors (other than l) in the three terms.

$$3x^2 \quad + \quad x \quad + \quad (-2)$$
$$\mathbf{ax^2} \quad + \quad \mathbf{bx} \quad + \quad \mathbf{c} \qquad \text{general form of a trinomial}$$
$$a = 3 \qquad\qquad b = 1 \qquad\qquad c = -2$$

Step 1. Find two numhers whose product is equal to the product of **a** times **c**, and whose sum is equal to **b**.

$$a \cdot c = (3x) \cdot (-2) = -6 \qquad b = 1$$

Factors of (-6)	Sum of Factors
1(-6) = -6	1 + (-6) = -5
2(-3) = -6	2 + (-3) = -1
(-1)(6) = -6	(-1) + 6 = 5
(-2)(3) = -6	**(-2) + 3 = 1**

Step 2. Rewrite the **bx** term using the above factors.
$$x = -2x + 3x$$

Step 3. Factor by grouping.
$$3x^2 - 2x \qquad + \qquad 3x - 2$$
(x is common)   (1 is common)

$$x(3x - 2) + 1(3x - 2)$$
[(3x - 2) is common]

The factors are $(3x - 2)(x + 1)$
$$3x^2 + x - 2 = (3x - 2)(x + 1) \qquad\qquad \textbf{Factored}$$

Example 2. Factor $3x^2 - 7x + 2$.

Solution: There are no common factors other than 1.
$$3x^2 + (-7)x + 2$$

Step 1. $ax^2 + b + c$
$$a = 3 \qquad\qquad b = -7 \qquad\qquad c = 2$$

$$a \cdot c = (3)(2) = 6 \qquad\qquad b = -7$$

Factors of (6)	Sum of Factors
(1)(6) = 6	1 + 6 = 7
(2)(3) = 6	2 + 3 = 5
(-1)(-6) = 6	**-1 + (-6) = -7**
(-2)(-3) = 6	-2 + (-3) = -5

Step 2. $-7x = -lx + (-6x)$

Step 3. $3x^2 - 1x$ + $(-6x) + 2$
             (x is common)   (-2 is common)

             $x(3x - 1) - 2(3x - 1)$
             [(3x - 1) is common]

             The factors are $(3x - 1)(x - 2)$

             $3x^2 - 7x + 2 = (3x - 1)(x - 2)$ **Factored**

Example 3.   Factor $6m^2 + 23m + 20$.

Solution: There are no common factors other than 1. We must find two numbers whose product is 6 • 20 or 120 and whose sum is 23. The numbers are 8 and 15.

             Factors of 120   **Sum of Factors**
             $(8)(15) = 120$ $8 + 15 = 23$

             Rewrite 23m as 8m + 15m:
                         $6m^2 + 23m + 20$
                         $6m^2 + 8m + 15m + 20$
                         $2m(3m + 4) + 5(3m + 4)$

             The factors are $(3m + 4)(2m + 5)$.
             $6m^2 + 23m + 20 = (3m + 4)(2m + 5)$ **Factored**

Exercise Set 5.4

Factor completely. If an expression cannot be factored, so state.

1) $3x^2 - x - 2$ 2) $2m^2 - 7m + 3$
3) $3x^2 - 8x + 5$ 4) $7t^2 + 20t - 3$
5) $5y^2 + 2y - 3$ 6) $4x^2 - 5x + 1$
7) $3x^2 - 5x + 2$ 8) $2c^2 + 5c - 7$
9) $2m^2 - m - 3$ 10) $6c^2 - 11c - 3$
11) $12u^2 - 11uv + 2v^2$ 12) $20a^2 + 7ab - 3b^2$
13) $18x^2 + 3xy - 10y^2$ 14) $10a^2 - 9ab - 9b^2$
15) $42x^2 + 4xy - 6y^2$ 16) $56y^2 + 5yz - 6z^2$
17) $6b^2 - 3b - 84$ 18) $12y^2 + 4y - 16$
19) $10m^2 - 24m + 8$ 20) $4x^2 - 1x - 5$

Answers for Exercise Set 5.4.

1) $(x - 1)(3x + 2)$ 2) $(m - 3)(2m - 1)$
3) $(x - 1)(3x - 5)$ 4) $(t + 3)(7t - 1)$
5) $(y + 1)(5y - 3)$ 6) $(x - 1)(4x - 1)$
7) $(x - 1)(3x - 2)$ 8) $(c - 1)(2c + 7)$
9) $(m + 1)(2m - 3)$ 10) Cannot be factored.

11) $(3u - 2v)(4u - v)$ 12) $(4a - b)(5a + 3b)$

13) $(3x - 2y)(6x + 5y)$ 14) $(2a - 3b)(5a + 3b)$

15) $2(3x - y)(7x + 3y)$ 16) $(8y + 3z)(7y - 2z)$

17) $3(2b + 7)(b - 4)$ 18) $4(y - 1)(3y + 4)$

19) $2(5m - 2)(m - 2)$ 20) $(x + 1)(4x - 5)$

Section 5.5 Special factoring formulas and a general review of factoring.

Summary:

> **Difference of Two Squares**
> $$a^2 - b^2 = (a + b)(a - b)$$

Example 1.   Factor each of the following using the difference of two squares formula.

a) $m^2 - 9$ b) $4m2 - 25$

c) $16x^2y^2 - 9$ d) $49x^2 - 9y2$

Solution: a) $a^2 - b^2 = (a)^2 - (b)^2 = (a + b)(a - b)$

$m^2 - 9 = (m)^2 - (3)^2 = (m + 3)(m - 3)$ **Factored**

b) $a^2 - b^2 = (a)^2 - (b)^2 = (a + b)(a - b)$

$4m^2 - 25 = (2m)^2 - (5)^2 = (2m + 5)(2m - 5)$

c) $a^2 - b^2 = (a)^2 - (b)^2 = (a + b) (a - b)$

$16x^2y^2 - 9 = (4xy)^2 - (3)^2 = (4xy + 3)(4xy - 3)$

d) $a^2 - b^2 = (a)^2 - (b)^2 = (a + b)(a - b)$

$49x^2 - 9y^2 = (7x)^2 - (3y)^2 = (7x + 3y)(7x - 3y)$

Summary:

> **Sum of two cubes**
> $$a^3 + b^3 = (a + b)(a^2 - ab + b^2)$$
>
> **Difference of two cubes**
> $$a^3 - b^3 = (a - b)(a^2 + ab + b^2)$$

Example 2.   Factor using the sum of two cubes formula or the difference of two cubes formula.

a) $8x^3 + y^3$ b) $8x^3 - 1$

c) $w^3 - 125b^3$ d) $27x^3 + 216x^3y^3$

Solution: a) $a^3 + b^3 = (a)^3 + (b)^3$ $= (a + b)(a2 - ab + b^2)$
             $8x^3 + y^3 = (2x)^3 + (y)^3$ $= (2x + y)[(2x)^2 - (2x)(y) + (y)^2]$
                                                    $= (2x + y)(4x^2 - 2xy + y^2)$ **Factored**

             b) $a^3 - b^3 = (a)^3 - (b)^3$ $= (a - b)(a^2 + ab + b^2)$
             $8x^3 - 1 = (2x)^3 - (1)^3$ $= (2x - 1)[(2x)^2 + (2x)(1) + (1)^2]$
                                                    $= (2x - 1)(4x^2 + 2x + 1)$ **Factored**

             c) $a^3 - b^3 = (a)^3 - (b)^3$ $= (a - b)(a^2 + ab + b^2)$
             $w^3 - 125b^3 = (w)^3 - (5b)^3$ $= (w - 5b)[(w)^2 + (w)(5b) + (5b)^2]$
                                                    $= (w - 5b)(w^2 + 5wb + 25b^2)$
                                                                          Factored

             d) $a^3 + b^3 = (a)^3 + (b)^3 = (a + b)(a^2 - ab + b^2)$

                $27x^3 + 216x^3y^3$ GCF is $27x^3$
                $27x^3 + 216x^3y^3$ $= 27x^3(1 + 8y^3)$
                                            $= 27x^3[(1)^3 + (2y)^3]$
                                            $= 27x^3[(1 + 2y)(1 - 2y + 4y^2)]$
                                                                          Factored

Exercise Set 5.5

Factor the difference of two squares.
   1) $x^2 - 4$ 2) $y^2 - 49$
   3) $64x^2 - 9y^2$ 4) $4b^2z^4 - 36y^6$
   5) $9 - 16x^2y^4$ 6) $y^4 - 16$

Factor the sum or difference of two cubes.
   7) $a^3 + 1$ 8) $a^3 + 27b^3$
   9) $x^3 - 1$ 10) $8a^3 + 27b^3$
   11) $27t^3 - 27$ 12) $125x^3 + 8z^6$

Factor each of the following completely.
   13) $5x^2 - 5$ 14) $3x^2 - 75$
   15) $y - 9y^3$ 16) $3x^3 - 12x^2 + 9x$
   17) $x^3 + 6x^2 + 8x$ 18) $5x^2 + 4x + x^3$
   19) $7x^3 - 7$ 20) $3y^3 + 81$

Answers for Exercise Set 5.5
   1) $(x + 2)(x - 2)$ 2) $(y + 7)(y - 7)$
   3) $(8x + 3y)(8x - 3y)$ 4) $(2bz^2 + 6y^3)(2bz^2 - 6y^3)$
   5) $(3 + 4xy^2)(3 - 4xy^2)$ 6) $(y^2 + 4)(y + 2)(y - 2)$
   7) $(a + 1)(a^2 - a + 1)$ 8) $(a + 3b)(a^2 - 3ab + 9b^2)$
   9) $(x - 1)(x^2 + x + 1)$ 10) $(2a + 3b)(4a^2 - 6ab + 9b^2)$
   11) $27(t - 1)(t^2 + t + 1)$ 12) $(5x + 2z^2)(25x^2 - 10xz^2 + 4z^4)$
   13) $5(x + 1)(x - 1)$ 14) $3(x + 5)(x - 5)$

15) $y(1 + 3y)(1 - 3y)$ 16) $3x(x - 1)(x - 3)$

17) $x(x + 4)(x + 2)$ 18) $x(x + 1)(x + 4)$

19) $7(x - 1)(x^2 + x + 1)$ 20) $3(y + 3)(y^2 - 3y + 9)$

Section 5.6   Solving Quadratic Equations Using Factoring

Summary:

> **Quadratic Equation**   Quadratic equations have the form
> $$ax^2 + bx + c = 0$$
> where **a, b** and **c** are real numbers, $a \neq 0$.
>
> Quadratic equations like those given above, where one side of the equation is written in descending order of the variable and the other side of the equation equal to zero is said to be in **standard form.**
>
> Some quadratic equations can be solved by factoring. Two methods that can be used to solve quadratic equations that cannot be solved by factoring are given in Chapter 10. To solve a quadratic equation by factoring we use the zero-factor property.
>
> **Zero-factor Property**
> If **ab** = 0 then **a** = 0 or **b** = 0.
>
> In other words, if the product of two factors is 0, then at least one of the factors must be 0.

Example 1.   Solve the equation $(x - 7)(x + 3) = 0$ using the Zero-factor Property.

Solution:

$(x - 7)(x + 3) = 0$

$x - 7 = 0$ or $x + 3 = 0$

$x - 7 + (?) = 0 + 7$ $x + 3 + (?) = 0 + (-3)$

$x = 7$ or $x = -3$

Thus is $x = 7$ or -3, the product of the factors is 0.
The solutions to the equations are 7 and -3.

Answer for (?) in Example 1.   7 , (-3)

Summary:

> **To Solve Quadratic Equation Using Factoring**
>
> 1) Write the equation in standard form with the squared term positive. This will result in the one side of the equation being equal to 0.
>
> 2) Set each factor containing a variable equal to zero and find the solution.

Example 2. Solve the equation $y^2 - 4y = 0$

Solution: Since the equation is written in standard form, factor the left side of the equation.

$$y^2 - 4y = 0$$
$$y(y - 4) = 0$$
$$y = 0 \quad \text{or} \quad y - 4 = 0 \qquad \textbf{Zero-factor Property}$$
$$y = 0 \quad \text{or} \quad y = 4$$

The solutions to the equation are 0 and 4.

Example 3. Solve the equation $y^2 + 6y = 55$

Solution: Write the equation in standard form.

$$y^2 + 6y = 55$$
$$y^2 + 6y + (?) = 55 + (-55)$$
$$y^2 + 6y - 55 = 0$$
$$(y + 11)(y - 5) = 0$$
$$y + 11 = 0 \quad \text{or} \quad y - 5 = 0 \qquad \textbf{Zero-factoring Property}$$

$$y = -11 \text{ or} \quad y = 5$$

The solutions to the equation are 5 and (-11).

Answer to (?) in Example 3.   (-55)

Example 4. Solve the equation $2x^2 + 8x = 24$.

Solution: Write the equation in standard form.

$$2x^2 + 8x = 24$$
$$2x^2 + 8x - 24 = 24 + (?)$$
$$2x^2 + 8x - 24 = 0 \qquad\qquad \textbf{GCF is 2}$$

$2(x^2 + 4x - 12) = 0$ **Factor again.**

$2(x + 6)(x - 2) = 0$

$x + 6 = 0$ or $x - 2 = 0$ **Zero-factoring Property**

$x = -6$ or $x = 2$

The solutions to the equation are (-6) and 2.

Answers to (?) in Example 4.   (-24)

Example 5.   Solve the equation $x^2 = 25$

Solution: Write the equation in standard form.

$x^2 = 25$

$x^2 + (?) = 25 + (-25)$

$x^2 - 25 = 0$ **Standard Form**

$(x + (?))(x - (?)) = 0$ **Factored**

$x + 5 = 0$ or $x - 5 = 0$ **Zero-factoring Property**

$x = -5$ or $x = 5$

The solutions to the equation are (-5) and 5.

Answer to (?) in Example 5.   (-25) ; 5 ; 5

Example 6.   Find two consecutive integers whose product is 240.

Let n = 1st integer

Let $n + 1$ = 2nd integer

(1st integer) • (2nd integer) = 240

$n(n + 1) = 240$

$n^2 + 1n = 240$

$n^2 + 1n - 240 = 0$ **Standard Form**

$(n - 15)(n + 16) = 0$ **Factored**

$n - 15 = 0$ or $n + 16 = 0$ **Zero-factoring Property**

$n = 15$ or $n = -16$

Thus the numbers are 15 and 16 or (-15) and (-16).

Exercise Set 5.6

Solve each equation.

1) $x(x - 5) = 0$ 2) $6x(3x - 2) = 0$

3) $(x + 3)(x - 7) = 0$ 4) $(2x + 1)(3x - 7) = 0$

5) $x^2 - 25 = 0$ 6) $4x^2 - 49 = 0$

7) $9x^2 = 16$ 8) $x^2 = 49$

9) $r^2 - 11r = 0$ 10) $3z^2 - 27z = 0$

11) $x^2 = 2x + 63$ 12) $z^2 - 12z + 32 = 0$

13) $4x^2 = 8x + 21$ 14) $x^2 - 3x - 10 = 0$

15) $y^2 - 14 = 5y$ 16) $z^2 - 8z + 15 = 0$

17) Find two consecutive odd integers whose product is 255.

18) The sum of the squares of two consecutive integers is 265. Find the numbers.

19) The length of a rectangle is 12 inches more than the width. Find the dimensions if the area is 85 square inches.

20) The length of a rectangle measures 15 inches more than its width. Find the dimensions of the rectangle if it has an area of 324 square inches .

Answers to Exercise Set 5.6

1) $x = 0$, $x = 5$	2) $x = 0$, $x = \frac{2}{3}$
3) $x = -3$, $x = 7$	4) $x = -\frac{1}{2}$, $x = \frac{7}{3}$
5) $x = -5$, $x = 5$	6) $x = -\frac{7}{2}$, $x = \frac{7}{2}$
7) $x = -\frac{4}{3}$, $x = \frac{4}{3}$	8) $x = -7$, $x = 7$
9) $r = 0$, $r = 11$	10) $z = 0$, $z = 9$
11) $x = -7$, $x = 9$	12) $z = 4$, $z = 8$
13) $x = \frac{-3}{2}$, $x = \frac{7}{2}$	14) $x = -2$, $x = 5$
15) $y = -2$, $y = 7$	16) $z = 3$, $z = 5$
17) 15, 17 or -15, -17	18) 11, 12 or -11, -12
19) 5, 17	20) 12, 27

Practice Test Chapter 5

1) Find the greatest common factor of $3w^2y^2$, $18wy^3$, and $27y^4$.

2) Find the greatest common factor of $4a^2x^2$, $16a^2x$, and $4a^2$.

Factor completely.

3) $4x - 2$	4) $9 - 27u^2$
5) $3a^2 - 9ab + 9ab^2$	6) $ab - 4b - 2a + 8$
7) $x^2 + cx + ax + ac$	8) $x^2 - 36$
9) $5 - 125c^2$	10) $x^2 + 6x + 9$
11) $m^2 + 12m + 36$	12) $4x^2 + 4x + 1$
13) $4m^2 + 24m + 36$	14) $9x^2 - 36xy + 36y^2$
15) $b^2x^2 - 16b^2x + 64b^2$	16) $w^3 - 8$

Solve each equation.

17) $(x + 3)(2x - 9) = 0$
18) $m^2 - 8m - 9 = 0$
19) $2x^2 + 5x + 2 = 0$

20) The area of two squares is 765 square inches. The side of one square measures 3 inches more than the side of the of the square. Find the lengths of the sides of the two squares.

Answers for Practice Test Chapter 5.

1) $3y^2$
2) $4a^2$
3) $2(2x - 1)$
4) $9(1 - 3u^2)$
5) $3a(a - 3b + 3b^2)$
6) $(a - 4)(b - 2)$
7) $(x + c)(x + a)$
8) $(x + 6)(x - 6)$
9) $5(1 + 5c)(1 - 5c)$
10) $(x + 3)(x + 3)$
11) $(m + 6)(m + 6)$
12) $(2x + 1)(2x + 1)$
13) $4(m + 3)(m + 3)$
14) $9(x - 2y)(x - 2y)$
15) $b^2(x - 8)(x - 8)$
16) $(w - 2)(w^2 + 2w + 4)$
17) $-3, \frac{9}{2}$
18) $-1, 9$
19) $-\frac{1}{2}, -2$
20) $18, 21$

Chapter 6 Rational Expressions and Equations

Section 6.1   Reducing Rational Expressions

Summary:

> A Rational Expression (also called an algebraic fraction) is an alge-braic expression of the form p/q where **p** and **q** are polynomials and $q \neq 0$.
>
> For negative algebraic fractions.
> $$-a/b = -a/b = a/-b$$
>
> **To reduce Rational Expressions**
>
> 1) Factor both numerator and denominator as completely as possible.
> 2) Divide both the numerator and denominator by any common factors.

Example 1.   Reduce $(28xy^3z^3)/60x^4yz^3$ to its lowest terms.

Solution: $(4 \cdot 7 \cdot x \cdot y \cdot y^2 \cdot z^3)/(4 \cdot 15 \cdot x \cdot x^3 \cdot y \cdot z^3) = 7y^2/15x^3$
The numerator and denominator was divided by what common factor?
The common factor was **$4xyz^3$**.

Example 2.   Reduce $4x/(2x - 6y)$ to its lowest terms.

Solution: $4x/(2x - 6y) = (2 \cdot 2x)/2(x - 3y) = 2x/(x - 3y)$
The numerator and denominator was divided by what common factor?
The common factor was **2**.

Example 3.   Reduce $(b^2 - 2b - 15)/(b^2 - b - 12)$

Solution: $(b^2 - 2b - 15)/(b^2 - b - 12) = (b - 5)(b + 3)/(b - 4)(b + 3) = (b - 5)/(b - 4)$
The numerator and denominator was divided by what common factor?
The common factor was **(b + 3)**.

Example 4.   Reduce $(4x + 12)/(10x^2 + 30x)$

Solution: $(4x + 12)/(10x^2 + 30x) = 4(x + 3)/10x(x + 3) = 4/10x = 2 \cdot 2/2 \cdot 5x = 2/5x$
The numerator and denominator were divided by what common
factors? The common factors were **(x + 3)** and **2**.

Example 5.   Reduce $\frac{(x + 2y)(x + 2y)}{(-x - 2y)}$

Solution: $\frac{(x + 2y)(x + 2y)}{(-x - 2y)} = \frac{1(x + 2y)\cancel{(x + 2y)}}{-1\cancel{(x + 2y)}}$

$= -1(x + 2y) = (-x - 2y)$

The numerator and denominator were divided by what common factors?

The common factors were **(x + 2y) and 1.**

Exercise Set 6.1

Reduce each expression to its lowest terms.

1) $\frac{12x^2y^2}{36x^3y^2}$ 2) $\frac{42a^2b^3}{7a^2b^5}$

3) $\frac{(2a - 4b)}{6a}$ 4) $\frac{(8m + 8)}{(4m^2 - 4m)}$

5) $\frac{(x^2 - x)}{(x^2 + x)}$ 6) $\frac{(6m - 18)}{(2m^2 - 6m)}$

7) $\frac{(3x + 6)}{(4x + 8)}$ 8) $\frac{(3a^2 - 6ab)}{(2a^2b - 4ab^2)}$

9) $\frac{(m^4 + 3m^2)}{(m^4 - 9)}$ 10) $\frac{(y^2 - 2y - 3)}{(y^2 + 4y + 3)}$

11) $\frac{(3m^2 - 2m - 1)}{(2m^2 - m - 1)}$ 12) $\frac{(x^2 - 5x + 6)}{(x^2 - 4x + 3)}$

13) $\frac{(x^3 - 4x^2y + 4xy^2)}{(x^3 - 4xy^2)}$ 14) $\frac{(16x^2 - 36y^2)}{(8x^2 + 24xy + 18y^2)}$

Answers to Exercise Set 6.1

1) $\frac{1}{3x}$ 2) $\frac{6}{b^2}$

3) $\frac{(a - 2b)}{3a}$ 4) $\frac{2}{(m - 1)}$

5) $\frac{(x - 1)}{(x + 1)}$ 6) $\frac{3}{m}$

7) $\frac{3}{4}$ 8) $\frac{3}{2b}$

9) $\frac{m^2}{(m^2 - 3)}$ 10) $\frac{(y - 3)}{(y + 3)}$

11) $\frac{(3m + 1)}{(2m + 1)}$ 12) $\frac{(x - 2)}{(x - 1)}$

13) $\frac{(x - 2y)}{(x + 2y)}$ 14) $\frac{2(2x - 3y)}{(2x + 3y)}$

Section 6.2 Multiplication and Division of Rational Expressions.

Summary:

Multiplication

1) Factor all numerators and denominators as completely as possible.
2) Divide out common factors.
3) Multiply numerators together and multiply denominators together.

Example 1.   Multiply $\frac{8bx}{15ay} \cdot \frac{5by}{4ax}$

Solution: $\frac{\overset{2}{\cancel{8bx}}}{15ay} \cdot \frac{5by}{\underset{1}{\cancel{4ax}}}$ Divide out the x's and divide 8 and 4 by 4.

$\frac{2b}{\underset{3}{\cancel{15ay}}} \cdot \frac{5by}{a}$ Divide out the y's and divide 5 and 15 by 5.

$\frac{2b}{3a} \cdot \frac{b}{a} = \frac{2b \cdot b}{3a \cdot a} = \frac{2b^2}{3a^2}$ *Answer*

Example 2.   Multiply $\frac{2a^2b^3}{3xy^2} \cdot \frac{9x^3y^2}{8ab}$

Solution: $\frac{\cancel{2a} \cdot a \cdot \cancel{b} \cdot b^2}{\cancel{3} \cdot \cancel{x} \cdot \cancel{y^2}} \cdot \frac{3 \cdot \cancel{3} \cdot \cancel{x} \cdot x^2 \cdot \cancel{y^2}}{\cancel{2} \cdot 4 \cdot \cancel{a} \cdot \cancel{b}} = \frac{3ab^2x^2}{4}$ *Answer*

What were the common factors?
The common factors were **2, 3, a, b, x, and y^2.**

Example 3.   Multiply $\frac{9}{(3x - 9)} \cdot \frac{(5x - 15)}{12}$

Solution: $\frac{9}{(3x - 9)} \cdot \frac{(5x - 15)}{12} = \frac{\overset{1}{\cancel{3}} \cdot \overset{1}{\cancel{3}}}{\underset{1}{\cancel{3}}\underset{1}{(\cancel{x - 3})}} \cdot \frac{5\overset{1}{(\cancel{x - 3})}}{\underset{1}{\cancel{3}} \cdot 4} = \frac{5}{4}$ *Answer*

What were the common factors?
The common factors were **(x - 3) , and 3.**

Example 4.   Multiply $\frac{(4x^2 + 16x)}{15xy} \cdot \frac{5xy^3}{(x + 4)}$

Solution: $\frac{4x^2 + 16x}{15xy} \cdot \frac{5xy^3}{x + 4}$

$= \frac{4x\overset{1}{(\cancel{x + 4})}}{\underset{1}{\cancel{5}} \cdot 3 \cdot \underset{11}{\cancel{xy}}} \cdot \frac{\overset{1}{\cancel{5}}\overset{1}{\cancel{x}} \cdot \overset{1}{\cancel{y}} \cdot y^2}{\underset{1}{(\cancel{x + 4})}} = \frac{4xy^2}{3}$ *Answer*

What were the common factors?
The common factors were **(x + 4), 5, x, and y.**

Example 5.   Multiply $(t^2 - t - 6)/(2t^2 + 8t + 8) \cdot 6/(4t^2 - 36)$

Solution: $(t^2 - t - 6)/(2t^2 + 8t + 8) \cdot 6/(4t^2 - 36)$

$$= \frac{\overset{1}{(t-3)}\overset{1}{(t+2)}}{\underset{1}{2}(t+2)\underset{1}{(t+2)}} \cdot \frac{\overset{3}{6}}{4(t+3)\underset{1}{(t-3)}} = 3/4(t+2)(t+3) \quad \textbf{\textit{Answer}}$$

What were the common factors?
The common factors were **(t - 3), (t + 2), and 2**.

Example 6.   Multiply $(4x^2 + 8x + 3)/(12x^2 - 30x + 18) \cdot (6x^2 - 9x)/(1 - 4x^2)$

Solution: $(4x^2 + 8x + 3)/(12x^2 - 30x + 18) \cdot (6x^2 - 9x)/(1 - 4x^2)$

$$= (2x + 1)(2x + 3)/6(2x - 3)(x - 1) \cdot 3x(2x - 3)/-1(4x^2 - 1)$$

$$= \frac{\overset{1}{(2x+1)}(2x+3)}{\underset{2}{6}\underset{1}{(2x-3)}(x-1)} \cdot \frac{3x\overset{1}{(2x-3)}}{-1\overset{1}{(2x+1)}(2x-1)}$$

$$= x(2x + 3)/2(2x - 1)(x - 1) \quad \textbf{\textit{Answer}}$$

What were the common factors?
The common factors were **(2x + 1), (2x - 3) and 3**.

Summary:

> **Division** $a/b \div c/d = a/b \cdot d/c = ad/bc$
>
> **To Divide Rational Expressions**
> Invert the divisor (the second fraction) and multiply.

Example 7.   Divide $6m^2 t^3/5c^4d \div 2mt/25c^2d^3$

Solution: $6m^2 t^3/5c^4d \div 2mt/25c^2d^3 = 6m^2 t^3/5c^4d \cdot 25c^2 d^3/2mt$

$$= \frac{\overset{3m}{6m^2}\overset{t^2}{t^3}}{\underset{1c^2}{5c^4d}} \cdot \frac{\overset{5}{25c^2}\overset{d^2}{d^3}}{\underset{1}{2mt}} = 3 \cdot 5 \cdot m \cdot t^2 \cdot d^2/c^2$$

$$= 15mt^2d^2/c^2 \quad \textbf{\textit{Answer}}$$

What were the common factors?
The common factors were **2, 5, m, c², d, and t**.

Example 8. Divide $\frac{(m^2 - 36)}{(m^2 - 4)} \div \frac{(m + 6)}{(m + 2)}$

Solution: $\frac{(m^2 - 36)}{(m^2 - 4)} \div \frac{(m + 6)}{(m + 2)} = \frac{(m^2 - 36)}{(m^2 - 4)} \cdot \frac{(m + 2)}{(m + 6)}$

$$= \frac{\overset{1}{(m + 6)}(m - 6)}{\underset{1}{(m + 2)}(m - 2)} \cdot \frac{\overset{1}{(m + 2)}}{\underset{1}{(m + 6)}} = \frac{(m - 6)}{(m - 2)} \quad \textbf{\textit{Answer}}$$

What were the common factors?
The common factors were **(m + 6)** and **(m + 2)**.

Example 9. Divide $\frac{(x^2 - 4x - 21)}{(x^2 - 6x - 16)} \div \frac{(2x - 14)}{(x^2 + 2x)}$

Solution: $\frac{(x^2 - 4x - 21)}{(x^2 - 6x - 16)} \div \frac{(2x + 14)}{(x^2 + 2x)} = \frac{(x^2 - 4x - 21)}{(x^2 - 6x - 16)} \cdot \frac{(x^2 + 2x)}{(2x - 14)}$

$$= \frac{\overset{1}{(x - 7)}(x + 3)}{(x - 8)\underset{1}{(x + 2)}} \cdot \frac{x\overset{1}{(x + 2)}}{2\underset{1}{(x - 7)}} = \frac{x(x + 3)}{2(x - 8)} \quad \textbf{\textit{Answer}}$$

What were the common factors?
The common factors were **(x + 2), and (x - 7)**.

Exercise Set 6.2

Multiply as indicated.

1) $\frac{15x}{8y} \cdot \frac{4y}{5x}$

2) $\frac{4x^2}{7y^3} \cdot \frac{35y}{12}$

3) $\frac{6a^2}{5e} \cdot \frac{35c^4}{24a^3}$

4) $\frac{15m^3}{27r^4} \cdot \frac{6r^4}{14m^3}$

5) $\frac{(5x - 5y)}{(x + 2y)} \cdot \frac{(2x + 4y)}{(x - y)}$ 6) $\frac{3x}{(x + y)} \cdot \frac{(x^2 - y^2)}{x^3}$

7) $\frac{(a^2 - a)}{b^2} \cdot \frac{b^3}{(a - 1)}$ 8) $\frac{(t^2 - 6t - 16)}{(t^2 + 4t - 21)} \cdot \frac{(t^2 - 8t + 15)}{(t^2 + 9t + 14)}$

9) $\frac{(4y^2 - 12y)}{(2y^2 - 9y + 9)} \cdot \frac{(2y^2 + 3y - 9)}{(4y^2 - 36)}$

10) $\frac{(x - 5)}{(x^2 + 2x - 3)} \cdot \frac{(x^2 + 5x - 6)}{(x^2 - 3x - 10)}$

Divide as indicated.

11) $\frac{36z^2}{7x} \div \frac{1}{3x}$

12) $12x^3 \div \frac{24x}{33y^2}$

13) $\frac{18x^2y^3}{125wz} \div \frac{81xy^5}{25w^3z}$

14) $\frac{(9m + 9)}{(8m - 24)} \div \frac{(3m + 3)}{(4m - 12)}$

15) $\frac{(10m + 20)}{(3m - 3)} \div \frac{(5m + 10)}{(6m - 6)}$

16) $\frac{(a + 4)}{(4 - a^2)} \div \frac{(a^2 - 16)}{(a - 2)}$

17) $\frac{(5r+15)}{(r^2-9)} \div \frac{(5r-15)}{(r^2-6r+9)}$

18) $\frac{(18-6x)}{(5x+10)} \div \frac{(x^2-6x+9)}{(x^2+5x+6)}$

19) $\frac{(4a^2+8a+3)}{(2a^2-5a+3)} \div \frac{(1-4a^2)}{(6a^2-9a)}$

20) $\frac{(x^2+2x-3)}{(x^2-2x-15)} \div \frac{(x^2+6x+9)}{(x^2-4x-5)}$

Answers to Exercise Set 6.2

1) $\frac{3}{2}$ 2) $\frac{5x^2}{3y^2}$ 3) $\frac{7c^4}{4ae}$ 4) $\frac{5}{21}$

5) 10   6) $\frac{3(x-y)}{x^2}$ 7) ab

8) $\frac{(t-8)(t-5)}{(t+7)(t+7)}$ or $\frac{(t-8)(t-5)}{(t+7)^2}$ 9) $\frac{y}{y-3}$

10) $\frac{x+6}{(x+3)(x-5)}$ 11) $\frac{108z^2}{7}$ 12) $\frac{33x^2y^2}{2}$

13) $\frac{2xw^2}{45y^2}$ 14) $\frac{3}{2}$ 15) 4   16) $\frac{-1}{(a+2)(a-4)}$

17) 1   18) $\frac{-6(x+3)}{5(x-3)}$ 19) $\frac{-3a(2a+3)}{(a-1)(2a-1)}$

20) $\frac{(x+1)(x-1)}{(x+3)(x+3)}$ or $\frac{(x+1)(x-1)}{(x+3)^2}$

Section 6.3 Addition and Subtraction of Rational Expressions with a Common Denominator.

Summary:

Addition and Subtraction

$$\frac{a}{c} + \frac{b}{c} = \frac{a+b}{c}, c \neq 0 \qquad \frac{a}{c} - \frac{b}{c} = \frac{a-b}{c}, c \neq 0$$

To Add or Subtract Expressions with a Common Denominator
1) Add or subtract the numerators.
2) Place the sum or difference of the numerators found in step 1 over the common denominator.
3) Reduce the fraction if possible.

Example 1.   Add $\frac{9}{8t} + \frac{3}{8t}$

Solution: $\frac{9}{8t} + \frac{3}{8t} = \frac{9+3}{8t} = \frac{(?)}{8t} = \frac{3}{2t}$ *Answer*

Answer to (?) in Example 1. is **12**.

Example 2.   Add $x/(x^2-1) + 1/(x^2-1)$

Solution:

$$x/(x^2-1) + 1/(x^2-1) = (x+1)/(x^2-1)$$
$$= (x+1)/(?)(?) \qquad \textit{Reduce}$$
$$= 1/(x-1) \qquad \textit{Answer}$$

Answers to (?) in Example 2. $(x+1)$ $(x-1)$.

Example 3.   Subtract $t/(t+4) - 2t/(t+4)$

Solution: $t/(t+4) - 2t/(t+4) = (t-2t)/(t+4) = -t/(t+4)$ *Answer*

Example 4.   Subtract $x^2/(x^2-9) - (x+6)/(x^2-9)$

Solution: $x^2/(x^2-9) - (x+6)/(x^2-9) = [x^2-(x+6)]/(x^2-9) = (x^2-x-6)/(x^2-9)$
$$= (?)(?)/(x+3)(x-3) \qquad \textit{Reduce}$$
$$= (x+2)/(x+3) \qquad \textit{Answer}$$

Answers to (?) in Example 4. $(x-3)$ $(x+2)$.

Exercise Set 6.3

Add or subtract as indicated. If possible, reduce all answers.

1) $2/(x-1) + 3x/(x-1)$ 2) $(2y+5)/(2y-1) + (-6)/(2y-1)$

3) $2t/(t+3) - 4t/(t+3)$ 4) $-2y/(y^2-36) - (3y-6)/(y^2-36)$

5) $m/(m-4) - 4/(m-4)$ 6) $(x+1)/(a+b) + (x-1)/(a+b)$

7) $2/(y+1) + 2/(y+1)$ 8) $(a+2)/(2a+1) + (1-a)/(2a+1)$

9) $(z+4)/(a-b) - (z+3)/(a-b)$ 10) $(6x-1)/(3x-2) - (3x+1)/(3x-2)$

11) $4a/(2a+3) + 6/(2a+3)$ 12) $4x^2/(x^2+3x+5) = (12x+20)/(x^2+3x+5)$

Answers to Exercise Set 6.3

1) $(3x+2)/(x-1)$ 2) 1 3) $-2t/(t+3)$

4) $(-5y+6)/(y^2-36)$ 5) 1 6) $2x/(a+b)$

7) $4/(y+1)$ 8) $3/(2a+1)$ 9) $1/(a-b)$

10) 1 11) 2 12) 4

Section 6.4 Finding the Least Common Denominator

Summary:

To Find the Least Common Denominator of Rational Expressions

1) Factor each denominator completely. Factors in any given denominator that occur more than once should be expressed as powers [therefore, $(x + 5)(x + 5)$ should be expressed as $(x + 5)^2$].

2) List all different factors (other than 1) that appear in any of the denominators. When the same factor appears in more than one denominator, write the factor with the highest power that appears.

3) The least common denominator is the product of all the factors found in step 2.

Example 1.   Find the least common denominator:

$$^3/_{4x} + {}^2/_3$$

Solution: The common factors (Other than 1) are 4, 3, and x. List each factor with its highest power. The least common denominator (LCD) is the product of these factors.

$$\text{LCD} = 3 \cdot 4 \cdot x = 12x$$

Example 2.   Find the least common denominator:

$$^{(3m + 5s)}/_{3ms^2} - {}^{(5m + 2s)}/_{2m^2s}$$

Solution: The common factors (other than 1) are 3, 2, m, and s. List each factor with its highest power. The LCD is the product of these factors.

$$\text{LCD} = 3 \cdot 2 \cdot m^2 \cdot s^2 = 6m^2s^2$$

Example 3.   Find the least common denominator (LCD):

$$^c/_{(2c + 2d)} + {}^d/_{(3c + 3d)}$$

Solution: Factor both denominators.

$$^c/_{2(c + d)} + {}^d/_{3(c + d)}$$

Common factors (other than 1) are 2, 3, and (c + d).
LCD = $2 \cdot 3 \cdot (c + d) = 6(c + d)$.

Example 4. Find the LCD:

$$\frac{2}{(x^2 + 4x + 4)} - \frac{2}{(x^2 - 4x + 4)}$$

Solution: Factor both denominators.

$$\frac{2}{(?)(?)} - \frac{2}{(?)(?)}$$

$$\frac{2}{(x + 2)^2} - \frac{2}{(x - 2)^2}$$

Common factors (other than 1) are **(x + 2)** and **(x - 2)**.

$$LCD = (x + 2)^2(x - 2)^2$$

Answers for (?) in Example 4.
        (x + 2), (x + 2), (x - 2), (x - 2)

Exercise Set 6.4

Find the least common denominator for each expression.

1) $\frac{3}{2} + \frac{4}{y}$ 2) $\frac{9}{4w} + \frac{6}{5w}$

3) $\frac{4}{x} + \frac{7}{x^3}$ 4) $\frac{2}{a^2} + \frac{5}{a^4}$

5) $\frac{13}{3y} + \frac{7}{9y^2}$ 6) $\frac{3}{12u^3v^2} - \frac{10}{18uv^3}$

7) $\frac{6}{50x^3y^4} - \frac{10}{20x^2y^5}$ 8) $\frac{5}{a} + \frac{7a}{(a + 3)}$

9) $\frac{2}{b} + \frac{b}{(b + 6)}$ 10) $\frac{2x}{(2x + 4)} - \frac{3}{4x}$

11) $\frac{5}{3x} + \frac{7}{(3x + 6)}$ 12) $\frac{9x}{(x^2 + 4x + 4)} + \frac{2}{(x + 2)}$

13) $\frac{2}{(x^2 - 2x + 1)} - \frac{5x}{(x - 1)}$ 14) $\frac{(4x + 9)}{(x^2 - x - 12)} + \frac{(x - 6)}{(x^2 + 6x + 9)}$

Answers for Exercise Set 6.4

1) 2y   2) 20w   3) x^3

4) a^4 5) $9y^2$ 6) $36u^3v^3$

7) $100x^3y^5$ 8) a(a + 3)   9) b(b + 6)

10) 4x(x + 2)   11) 3x(x + 2)   12) $(x + 2)^2$

13) $(x - 1)^2$ 14) (x - 4)(x + 3)^2

Section 6.5 Addition and Subtraction of Rational Expressions.

Summary:

> **To Add or Subtract Two Rational Expressions with Unlike Denominators.**
>
> 1) Determine the Least Common Denominator (LCD).
>
> 2) Rewrite each fraction as an equivalent fraction with the LCD. This is done by multiplying both the numerator and denominator of each fraction by any factors needed to obtain the LCD.
>
> 3) Add or subtract the numerators while maintaining the LCD.
>
> 4) When possible factor the remaining numerator and reduce fractions.

Example 1. Add $3/a^2 + 7/a^3$

(Step 1) $\quad$ LCD $= a^3$

(Step 2) $\quad$ $\dfrac{3 \cdot a}{a^2 \cdot a} + \dfrac{7}{a^3} = \dfrac{3a}{a^3} + \dfrac{7}{a^3}$

(Step 3) $\quad$ $\dfrac{3a}{a^3} + \dfrac{7}{a^3} = \dfrac{(3a + 7)}{a^3}$ $\qquad$ *Answer*

Example 2. Add $5/6xy^2 + 2/8x^2y$

(Step 1) $\quad$ LCD $= 24x^2y^2$

(Step 2) $\quad$ $\dfrac{(5 \cdot 4x)}{(6xy^2 \cdot 4x)} + \dfrac{(2 \cdot 3y)}{(8x^2y \cdot 3y)} = \dfrac{20x}{24x^2y^2} + \dfrac{6y}{24x^2y^2}$

(Step 3) $\quad$ $\dfrac{20x}{24x^2y^2} + \dfrac{6y}{24x^2y^2} = \dfrac{(20x + 6y)}{24x^2y^2}$

(Step 4) $\quad$ $\dfrac{(20x + 6y)}{24x^2y^2} = \dfrac{2(10x + 3y)}{24x^2y^2} = \dfrac{(10x + 3y)}{12x^2y^2}$
$\qquad$ *Answer*

Example 3. Add $3/a + a/(a + 3)$

(Step 1) $\quad$ LCD $= a(a + 3)$

(Step 2) $\quad$ $\dfrac{3 \cdot (a + 3)}{a \cdot (a + 3)} + \dfrac{a \cdot a}{(a + 3) \cdot a} = \dfrac{(3a + 9)}{a(a + 3)} + \dfrac{a^2}{a(a + 3)}$

(Step 3) $\quad$ $\dfrac{(a^2 + 3a + 9)}{a(a + 3)}$ $\qquad$ *Answer*

Example 4.   Add $2x/(x^2 - 2x + 1) - 5/(x - 1)$

(Step 1) $LCD = (x - 1)^2 = (x - 1)(x - 1)$

(Step 2) $2x/(x - 1)(x - 1) - 5 \cdot (x - 1)/(x - 1) \cdot (x - 1)$

$2x/(x - 1)(x - 1) - (5x - 5)/(x - 1)(x - 1)$

(Step 3) $2x - (5x - 5)/(x - 1)(x - 1) = 2x + (-5x + 5)/(x - 1)(x - 1)$

$[2x + (-5x) + 5]/(x - 1)(x - 1) = (-3x + 5)/(x - 1)(x - 1)$

Answer

Exercise Set 6.5
Add or Subtract as indicated.

1) $7x/12 - 5x/9$

2) $1/r + 1/r^2$

3) $3/4x + 4/6x$

4) $(4x - 9)/8 - (3x - 8)/12$

5) $3/(4x - 6) + 4/(10x - 15)$

6) $1 + 3x/(2 - 3x)$

7) $1/(b^2 - ab) + 1/(ab - a^2)$

8) $4/4ab + 5/a^2b$

9) $9/5x^2y^2 - 3/10xy$

10) $4/(x - 1) + 5/(x + 3)$

11) $7/(2x - 3) - 6/(x - 5)$

12) $7/(4x - 6) + 12/(3x + 9)$

13) $15/(5y - 10) + 14/(2y + 4)$

14) $2/(y^2 - 4) + 1/(2y - y^2)$

15) $3/(x^2 - 3x + 2) - 2/(x^2 - 1)$

16) $x/(x^2 - 3x - 10) - 2/(x^2 - 6x + 5)$

17) $4/(x^2 - x - 6) + 5/(4 - x^2)$

18) $2/(y + 1) - 4y/(y^2 - 1)$

Answers for Exercise Set 6.5

1) $x/36$

2) $(r + 1)/r^2$

3) $17/12x$

4) $(6x - 11)/24$

5) $23/[10(2x - 3)]$

6) $2/(2 - 3x)$

7) $(a + b)/[ab(b - a)]$

8) $(a + 5)/a^2b$

9) $(18 - 3xy)/10x^2y^2$

10) $(9x + 7)/(x - 1)(x + 3)$

11) $(-5x - 17)/(x - 5)(2x - 3)$

12) $(23x - 3)/2(2x - 3)(x + 3)$

13) $(10y - 8)/(y + 2)(y - 2)$

14) $1/y(y + 2)$

15) $(x + 7)/(x + 1)(x - 1)(x - 2)$

16) $(x^2 - 3x - 4)/(x - 5)(x - 1)(x + 2)$

17) $(x - 7)/(x + 2)(x - 3)(2 - x)$

18) $-2/(y - 1)$

Section 6.6 Complex Fractions (Optional)

Summary:

To Simplify a Complex Fraction — Method 1

1) Add or subtract each secondary fraction as indicated to obtain a single fraction in both the numerator and the denominator.

2) Invert and multiply the denominator of the complex fraction by the numerator of the complex fraction.

3) Simplify when possible.

numerator of
complex fraction
$\updownarrow$
$$\frac{(a + b)/a}{(a - b)/a} \quad \text{main fraction line}$$
$\updownarrow$
denominator of
complex fraction

secondary
fractions
$$\left[\begin{array}{c} (a + b)/a \\ (a - b)/a \end{array} \right.$$

Example 1.   Simplify $\dfrac{5/6 + 1/3}{7/12 + 5/9}$

Solution: (Step 1)

$\rightarrow LCD = 6$ $\rightarrow LCD = 36$

$(5/6 + {}^{1 \cdot 2}/_{3 \cdot 2}) \Big/ ({}^{7 \cdot 3}/_{12 \cdot 3} + {}^{5 \cdot 4}/_{9 \cdot 4})$

$(5/6 + 2/6) \Big/ ({}^{21}/_{36} + {}^{20}/_{36}/36 = 7/6 \Big/ {}^{41}/_{36}$

(Step 2) $7/6 \cdot {}^{36}/_{41} = 7/6 \cdot \overset{6}{\underset{1}{{}^{36}}}/_{41} = {}^{42}/_{41}$ *Answer*

Example 1.   Simplify $(w + 1/x) / (1/w + x)$

$$\rightarrow LCD = x \qquad \rightarrow LCD = w$$

Solution: (Step 1) $(^w \cdot {}^x/_{1 \cdot x} + 1/x) \quad / \quad (1/w + {}^{x \cdot w}/_{1 \cdot w})$

$$(^{wx}/_x + 1/x) / (1/w + {}^{wx}/_w) = (^{wx + 1}/_x) / (^{1 + wx}/_w)$$

(Step 2) $\overset{1}{\overset{}{({\bcancel{wx+1}})}}/_x \cdot {}^w/_{\underset{1}{(\bcancel{wx+1})}} = {}^w/_x$ ***Answer***

Summary:

To Simplify a Complex Fraction — Method 2

1) Find the least common denominator of each of the two secondary fractions.

2) Next find the LCD of the complex fraction. The LCD of the complex fraction will be the two expressions found in step 1.

3) Multiply both secondary fractions by the LCD of the complex fraction found in step 2.

4) Simplify when possible.

Example 3.   Simplify $(^5/_6 + 1/_3) / (^7/_{12} + ^5/_9)$

Solution: (Step 1)   LCD of the numerator is 6 .
LCD of the denominator is 36 .

(Step 2)   LCD of the complex fraction is 36.
(Step 3) $36 (^5/_6 + 1/_3) / 36 (^7/_{12} + ^5/_9)$

$$[(\overset{6}{\bcancel{36}} \cdot {}^5/_6) + (\overset{12}{\bcancel{36}} \cdot 1/_3)] / [(\overset{3}{\bcancel{36}} \cdot {}^7/_{\bcancel{12}}) + (\overset{4}{\bcancel{36}} \cdot {}^5/_9)]$$

$$^{(30 + 12)}/_{(21 + 20)} = {}^{42}/_{41} \qquad \textit{Answer}$$

Example 4.   Simplify $(w + 1/x) / (1/w + x)$

Solution: (Step 1)   LCD of the numerator is x.
LCD of the denominator is w.

(Step 2)   LCD of the complex fraction is wx.

(Step 3) $wx(w + {}^1\!/_x)$ / $wx({}^1\!/_w + x)$

$[[wx \cdot (w)] + (wx \cdot {}^1\!/_x)]$ / $[(wx \cdot {}^1\!/_w) + [wx \cdot (x)]]$

$(w^2x + w)$ / $(x + wx^2)$

(Step 4) $w(\overset{1}{\cancel{wx+1}})$ / $x(\underset{1}{\cancel{1+wx}}) = {}^w\!/_x$ *Answer*

Exercise Set 6.6

Simplify each expression.

1) $(2 - {}^3\!/_5)$ / $(2 + {}^1\!/_{10})$ 2) $({}^1\!/_2 + {}^3\!/_4)$ / $({}^2\!/_3 + {}^5\!/_6)$

3) $(3 + {}^1\!/_7)$ / $(1 - {}^3\!/_{14})$ 4) $({}^3\!/_a - {}^2\!/_x)$ / $({}^5\!/_a - {}^6\!/_x)$

5) $({}^1\!/_x - {}^1\!/_y)$ / $({}^1\!/_x + {}^1\!/_y)$ 6) $(1 + {}^1\!/_x)$ / $(x + 1)$

7) $({}^x\!/_y - 1)$ / $({}^y\!/_x - 1)$ 8) $({}^1\!/_{x^2} - {}^1\!/_{y^2})$ / $({}^1\!/_x - {}^1\!/_y)$

9) $[{}^z\!/_{(z-1)} - 1]$ / $[1 + {}^z\!/_{(z-1)}]$ 10) $[v - {}^v\!/_{(v-1)} - 1]$ / $[{}^v\!/_{(v-1)} + 1]$

Answers for Exercise Set 6.6

1) ${}^2\!/_3$ 2) ${}^5\!/_6$

3) 4   4) ${}^{(3x-2a)}\!/_{(5x-6a)}$

5) ${}^{(y-x)}\!/_{(y+x)}$ 6) ${}^1\!/_x$

7) $-{}^x\!/_y$ 8) ${}^{(y+x)}\!/_{xy}$

9) ${}^1\!/_{(2z-1)}$ 10) ${}^{(v^2-2v)}\!/_{(2v-1)}$

Section 6.7 Solving Equations Containing Rational Expressions.

Summary:

> **To Solve Equations Containing Fractions**
> 1) Determine the LCD of all fractions in the equation.
>
> 2) Multiply **both** sides of the equation by the LCD. This will result in every term in the equation being multiplied by the LCD.
>
> 3) Remove any parentheses and combine like terms on each side of the equation.
>
> 4) Solve the equation using the properties discussed in earlier sections.
>
> 5) Check your solution in the original equation.

Example 1. Solve $^x/_2 + {}^x/_4 = 15$

Solution: (Step 1) $\text{LCD} = 4$

(Step 2) $4\,(^x/_2 + {}^x/_4) = 4(15)$

(Step 3) $(\overset{2}{4} \cdot {}^x/_{\underset{1}{2}}) + (\overset{1}{4} \cdot {}^x/_{\underset{1}{4}}) = 4(15)$

(Step 4) $2x + 1x = 60$
$3x = 60$
$x = (?)$ *Answer*

(Step 5)
$^x/_2 + {}^x/_4 = 15$
$^{(?)}/_2 + {}^{(?)}/_4 = 15$
$10 + 5 = 15$
$15 \quad = 15$ *True*

Answers for (?) in Example 1. Step 4) 20
Step 5) 20, 20

Example 2. Solve the equation. $^{(12-3x)}/_4 - {}^{(3x-11)}/_3 = 1$

Solution: (Step 1) $\text{LCD} = 12$

(Step 2) $12[^{(12-3x)}/_4 - {}^{(3x-11)}/_3)] = 12(1)$

(Step 3) $\overset{3}{\cancel{12}}[^{(12-3x)}/_{4_1}) + (\overset{-4}{\cancel{-12}})[^{(3x-11)}/_{3_1})] = 12(1)$
$3(12 - 3x) + (-4)(3x - 11) \quad = 12(1)$

$$(\text{Step 4}) \qquad 36 - 9x + (-12x) + 44 = 12$$
$$(?)x + 80 = 12$$
$$(?)x = -68$$
$$x = {}^{-68}/{}_{-21}$$
$$x = {}^{68}/{}_{21} \qquad \textit{Answer}$$

Answer for (?) in Example 2.

Step 4)   (-21), (-21)

Example 3.   Solve the equation. ${}^{30}/{}_{x} - {}^{18}/{}_{2x} = 7$

Solution: (Step 1) $LCD = 2x$

(Step 2) $2x({}^{30}/{}_{x} - {}^{18}/{}_{2x}) = 2x(7)$

(Step 3) $(2x)({}^{30}/{}_{x}) + (2x)({}^{-18}/{}_{2x}) = (2x)(7)$
$$2(30) + 1(-18) = (2x)(7)$$

(Step 4) $60 + (-18) = 14x$
$${}^{(60 - 18)}/{}_{14} = x$$
$${}^{42}/{}_{14} = x$$
$$3 = x \qquad \textit{Answer}$$

(Step 5) ${}^{30}/{}_{x} - {}^{18}/{}_{2x} = 7$
$${}^{30}/{}_{(?)} - {}^{18}/{}_{2(?)} = 7$$
$$10 - 3 = 7$$
$$7 = 7 \qquad \textit{True}$$

Answer for (?) in Example 2.   (Step 5)   3, 3

> **Warning:** Whenever **x** appears in any denominator, it is necessary to check your answer in the original equation. If the answer obtained makes any denominator equal to zero, that value is not a solution to the equation. Such values are called **extraneous roots** or **extraneous solutions.**

Exercise Set 6.7

Solve each equation and check your solution.

1) ${}^{x}/{}_{2} - {}^{x}/{}_{3} = 10$ 2) ${}^{(5x - 6)}/{}_{5} - {}^{3x}/{}_{4} = {}^{(x - 9)}/{}_{10}$

3) ${}^{1}/{}_{3x} = 6$ 4) ${}^{1}/{}_{4x} = 12$

5) ${}^{3}/{}_{x} = {}^{19}/{}_{3x} - {}^{5}/{}_{3}$ 6) ${}^{(3x + 1)}/{}_{4} = {}^{(13 - x)}/{}_{2}$

7) ${}^{(4x + 6)}/{}_{5} = {}^{(8x + 5)}/{}_{3}$ 8) ${}^{(x + 9)}/{}_{2x} = {}^{15}/{}_{x} - 3$

9) $^9/_{(2x+1)} = 3$

10) $^{10}/_{(1-2x)} = 2$

11) $^3/_x = ^2/_{(5-x)}$

12) $^{(x+3)}/_{(x+1)} = ^{(x+2)}/_{(x+4)}$

13) $^1/_{(x-5)} + ^1/_{(x+5)} = ^8/_{(x^2-25)}$

14) $^{(x+1)}/_{(x-3)} - ^{(2x-4)}/_{(x^2-9)} = 1$

Answers for Exercise Set 6.7

1) x = 60	2) x = 2	3) x = $^1/_{18}$
4) x = $^1/_{48}$	5) x = 2	6) x = 5
7) x = -$^1/_4$	8) x = 3	9) x = 1
10) x = -2	11) x = 3	12) x = -$^5/_2$
13) x = 4	14) x = -8	

Section 6.8 Applications of Rational Equations

Many applications of algebra involve rational equations. After you represent the application as an equation, you solve the rational equation as done in Section 6.7.

Example 1.   Determine two numbers such that their sum is 88 and one number is $^5/_6$ of the other.

Solution: Let x = first number
Let $^5/_6$x = second number

$$\begin{aligned}
(\text{first number}) + (\text{second number}) &= 88 \\
x \qquad + \qquad {}^5/_6 x &= 88 \\
6(x + {}^5/_6 x) &= 6(88) \\
6(x) + (6)({}^5/_6 x) &= 6(88) \\
6x + 5x &= 528 \\
11x &= 528 \\
x &= (?)
\end{aligned}$$

Since the first number is 48, the second number is $^5/_6$(48) or 40. The sum of 40 and 48 is 88.

Answer to (?) in Example 1.   48

Example 2.   The simple lens formula

$$^1/_{f_1} + ^1/_{f_2} = ^1/_f$$

gives the relation between the focal length of the lens f, the object distance f_1 and the image distance f_2.

If the object distance is 10 cm. and the image distance is 15 cm., find the focal length.

Solution: $\quad {}^1/_{f_1} + {}^1/_{f_2} = {}^1/_f$

$${}^1/_{10} + {}^1/_{15} = {}^1/_f$$

$$30f({}^1/_{10} + {}^1/_{15}) = 30f({}^1/_f)$$

$$30f({}^1/_{10}) + 30f({}^1/_{15}) = 30f({}^1/_f)$$

$$3f + 2f = 30$$
$$5f = 30$$
$$f = (?) \qquad \textbf{\textit{Answer}}$$

Answer for (?) in Example 2.   6 cm.

Example 3.   The area of a triangle is 180 square units. Find the base and height if the base is 6 more than three times its height.

Solution: Let x = height
Let 3x + 6 = base
area = $\frac{1}{2}$ (base) • (height)

$$180 = {}^1/_2(3x + 6)\,(x)$$
$$2(180) = 2\,[{}^1/_2(3x + 6)(x)]$$
$$360 = (3x + 6)(x)$$
$$360 = 3x^2 + 6x$$
$$0 = 3x^2 + 6x - 360$$
$$0 = 3(x^2 + 2x - 120)$$
$$0 = x^2 + 2x - 120$$
$$0 = (x + 12)(x - 10)$$
$$x + 12 = 0 \quad \text{or} \quad x - 10 = 0$$
$$x = -12 \qquad\qquad x = 10$$

Since the dimensions of a geometric figure cannot be negative, we can eliminate x = -12 as an answer to the problem.

height = x = 10
base = 3x + 6 = 3(10) + 6 = (?)

Check: area   = $\frac{1}{2}$ base • height
180   = 1(10) • (36)
180   = 180   ***True***

Answer for (?) in Example 3.   36

Example 4. Wes Sommerville's plane averaged 120 miles per hour on a flight from Rochester to Cleveland. On the return flight the average speed was 160 miles per hour. If the round trip was made in 7 hours, what is the distance between Rochester and Cleveland?

Solution: Let d = distance between Rochester and Cleveland

Plane	d	r	t
to Cleveland	d	120	$d/120$
to Rochester	d	160	$d/160$

$$
\begin{aligned}
\text{(time going)} \quad + \text{(time returning)} \quad &= \text{(total time)} \\
d/120 \quad + \quad d/160 \quad &= 7 \\
480\,(d/120 + d/160) &= 480(7) \\
480(d/120) + 480(d/160) &= 480(7) \\
(?)d + (?)d &= 3{,}360 \\
7d &= 3{,}360 \\
d &= (?)
\end{aligned}
$$

The distance between Rochester and Cleveland is 480 miles.

Answers for (?) in Example 4.   4, 3, 480

Exercise Set 6.8

Solve each problem.

1) Determine two numbers such that the sum of their reciprocals is 8, and one number is $1/3$ of the other.

2) Three times a number divided by the sum of the number and two is the same as the number minus two. Find the number.

3) Using the simple lens formula given in Example 2, determine the distance from the lens to the image if the focal length of a lens is 6.0 cm. and the object distance is 6.8 cm.

4) The formula $1/r = 1/r_1 + r/r_2$ gives the resistance r which is equivalent to the resistance of r_1 and r_2 when they are connected in parallel. What is the equivalent or effective resistance of resistances of 200 rhms and 300 rhms which are connected in parallel?

5) The area of a triangle is 119 square units. Find the base and height if the base is three more than the height.

6) The base of a triangle is 9 centimeters less than the height. Find the base and height if the triangle's area is 35 square centimeters.

7) If a plane with a cruising speed of 350 miles per hour can fly 480 miles with the wind in the same time that it can fly 360 miles against the wind, what is the velocity of the wind?

8) A Regal motor boat is set at a given rate. On the Genesee River which flows at the rate of 3 miles per hour, it can go 6 miles downstream in the same time as it can go 4 miles upstream. What is the rate of the motor boat in still water?

9) This past summer, Mike Sullivan had a swimming pool installed. A two-inch pipe could fill his pool in 8 hours, and a four-inch pipe could fill it in 2 hours. How long will it take for both to fill Mike's pool?

Answers for Exercise 6.8

1) $^1/_2$, $^1/_6$ 2) -1 , 4

3) 51 cm.   4) 120 rhms

5) 14 (height) , 17 (base)   6) 14 (height) , 5 (base)

7) 50 m.p.h.   8) 15 m.p.h.   9) 1.6 hours

Practice Test Chapter 6
Perform the operations indicated.

1) $^3/_{4a} - ^5/_{18a}$ 2) $^{(3x - 15)}/_{10} \div {^{(2x - 10)}/_{15}}$

3) $^{15}/_{(2 - 4x)} \cdot {^{(6x - 3)}/_{10}}$ 4) $^1/_{(9x^2 - 3xy)} \cdot {^1/_{(y^2 - 3xy)}}$

5) $^{(x^2 - 3x + 2)}/_{(2x^2 - 5x + 2)} \cdot {^{(x^2 - 2x - 8)}/_{(x^2 + x - 2)}}$

6) $^5/_{(6b - 3a)} - {^3/_{(2a - 4b)}}$

7) Simplify $(1 - {^{b^2}/_{a^2}}) / (1 - {^b/_a})$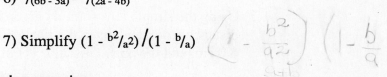

Solve each expression.

8) $^4/_{3x} - {^3/_{4x}} = {^7/_{16}}$ 9) $^1/_{(y + 5)} + {^2/_{(y - 1)}} = 0$

Solve the problem.

10) On the north branch of the Mouse River, Jimmie Miller can paddle his canoe 1 mile upstream in the same amount of time as it takes him to paddle 2 miles downstream. If he can paddle 3 miles per hour in still water, what is the rate of the current in the stream?

Answers for Practice Test Chapter 6

1) $^{17}/_{36a}$

2) $^9/_4$

3) $-^9/_4$

4) $^{(y-3x)}/_{[3xy(3x-y)]}$

5) $^{(x-4)}/_{(2x-1)}$

6) $^{-19}/_{[6(a-2b)]}$

7) $^{(a+b)}/_a$

8) $^4/_3$

9) -3

10) 1 mph

Chapter 7 Graphing Linear Equations

Section 7.1 The Cartesian Coordinate System

Summary:

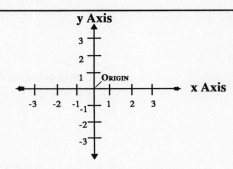

Origin — The point of intersection of the two axes.

Ordered Pair is a specific method used to describe the location of a point in the coordinate system. The ordered pair contains the **x** and **y** coordinates of a point placed in parentheses with the **x** coordinate listed first and the **y** coordinated listed last.

Example 1.   Plot each of the following on the same set of axes.

a) A (3, 5)   b) B (-5, 2)

c) C (-5, -4)   d) D (0, -3)

e) E (4, 6)   f) F (-3, 0)

Solution:

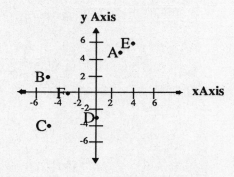

Example 2. List the ordered pairs for each point shown in the accompanying figure.

POINT	ORDERED PAIR
A	(-6, 4)
B	(2, 2)
C	(-4, 0)
D	(0, -4)
E	(0, 0)
F	(4, -6)

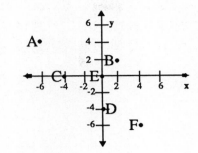

Exercise Set 7.1

1) List the ordered pairs corresponding to each of the following points.

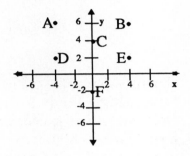

2) List the ordered pairs corresponding to each of the following points.

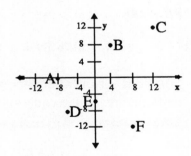

3) Plot each of the following points on the same set of axis.

  A (3, 1)   B (-4, -2)   C (0, 3)
  D (5, -4)   E (4, -3)   F (-2, 4)

4) Plot the following points. Then determine if the following points are all in a straight line.

  A (-6, -4)   B (-4, -2)   C (-2, 0)
  D (-2, 2)   E (2, 4)   F (4, 6)

Answers for Exercise Set 7.1

1) A (-4, 6)   B (4, 6)   C (0, 4)
    D (-4, 2)   E (4, 2)   F (0, -2)

2) A (-8, 0)   B (4, 8)   C (12, 12)
    D (6, -8)   E (0, -6)   F (8, -12)

3)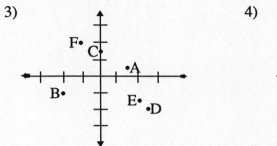

4)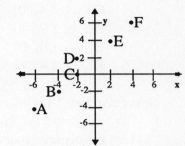

Not on a straight line.

Section 7.2 Graphing Linear Equations

Summary:

> A **linear equation in two variables** is an equation that can be put in the form
>
> $$ax + by = c \text{ (Standard Form)}$$
>
> Solutions for linear equation in two variables will be all the ordered pairs that make the equation true.

Example 1.   Determine which of the following ordered pairs satisfy the equation $y - x = 1$.

a) (0, 1)   b) (2, 3)   c) (5, 6)   d) (-3, -4)

Solution: To determine if the ordered pairs are solutions, we substitute them into the equation.

a)   (0, 1)   b)   (2, 3)
        $y - x = 1$ $y - x = 1$
        $(1) - (0) = 1$ $(3) - (2) = 1$
               $1 = 1$ $1 = 1$
        (0, 1) is a solution   (2, 3) is a solution

➥ **Note:**   Every Linear equation of the form **ax + by = c**
will be a straight line when graphed.

Graphing Linear Equations by Plotting Points

1) Solve the linear equation for the variable y. That is, get the variable y by itself on the left side of the equal sign.
2) Select a value for the variable x. Substitute this value in the equation for x and find the corresponding value of y. Record the ordered pair (x, y).
3) Repeat step 2 with two different values of x. This will give you two additional ordered pairs.
4) Plot the three ordered pairs. The three ordered pairs should be collinear. If they are not collinear, recheck your work for mistakes.
5) With a straight-edge, draw a straight line through the three points. Draw an arrow tip on each end of the line to show that the line continues indefinitely in both directions.

Example 2.   Graph the equation $y = \frac{2}{3}x - 2$

Solution: To obtain the graph of an equation in two variables determined solutions of the equation by assigning convenient values to one of the variables and solve the resulting equation for the corresponding values of the other variable.

Assigned Values of x	$y = \frac{2}{3}x - 2$	Ordered Pair
-3	$y = \frac{2}{3}(-3) - 2 = -4$	(-3, -4)
0	$y = \frac{2}{3}(0) - 2 = -2$	(0, -2)
3	$y = \frac{2}{3}(3) - 2 = 0$	(3, 0)
6	$y = \frac{2}{3}(6) - 2 = 2$	(6, 2)

Plot the points and draw the straight line.

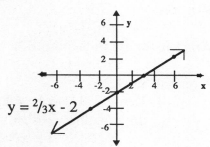

Graphing Linear Equations Using the x and y Intercepts

1) Find the y intercept by setting x equal to 0 and solving the resulting equation for y.
2) Find the x intercept by setting y equal to 0 and solving the resulting equation for x.
3) Determine a check point by selecting a nonzero value for x and finding the corresponding value for y.
4) Plot the y intercept (where the graph crosses the y axis), the x intercept (where the graph crosses the x axis), and the check point. The three points should be collinear. If not, recheck your work.
5) *Using a straight-edge,* draw a straight line through the three points. Draw an arrow tip at both ends of the line to show that the line continues indefinitely in both directions.

Example 3.   Graph the equation $y = \frac{2}{3}x - 2$ by plotting the x and y intercepts.

Solution:

$$y = \frac{2}{3}x - 2$$

(Step 1) $\quad y = \frac{2}{3}(0) - 2 = -2 \qquad$ ***(0, -2) y intercept***

(Step 2) $\quad (0) = \frac{2}{3}x - 2$

$$3(0) = 3\ \frac{2}{3}x - 2$$

$$0 = (?)x - 6$$

$$6 = 2x$$

$$(?) = x \qquad\qquad \textbf{\textit{(3, 0) x intercept}}$$

Now plot the x and y intercept and draw the straight line.

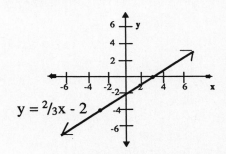

$$y = \frac{2}{3}x - 2$$

Answer for (?) in Example 3.   2,   3

Exercise Set 7.2

1) Determine which of the following ordered paris satisfy the equation $y = -\frac{4}{3}x + 4$

      a) (3, 0)   b) (0, 4)
      c) (2, 4)   d) $(\frac{3}{2}, 2)$

2) Determine which of the following ordered pairs satisfy
the equation y = 3x - 2.the equation y = 3x - 2.

a) (0, -2)   b) (²/₃, 0)   c) (2, 4)   d) (³/₂, 2)

Graph each equation by solving the equation for **y**, selecting three arbitrary
values for **x**, and finding corresponding values of **y**.

3) 2x + 3y = 6   4) 2x - y = 0
5) 4x - 3y = 12   6) 4x + 3y = -12
7) 2x + 5y = 10   8) 2x- 5y = 10

Graph each equation using x and y intercepts.

9) 2x + y = 2   10) 2x + 3y = -17

Answers for Exercise Set 7.2

1. a) yes   b) yes   c) no   d) yes
2. a) yes   b) yes   c) yes   d) no

3) y = -²/₃x + 2

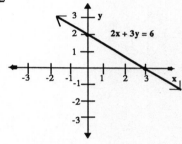

4) y = 2x

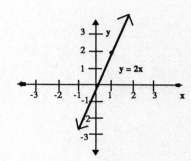

5) y = ⁴/₃x - 4

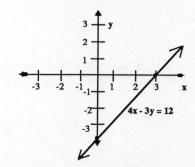

6) $y = -^4/_3x - 4$

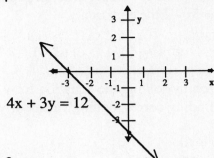

4x + 3y = 12

7) $y = -^2/_5x + 2$

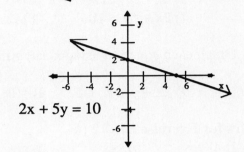

2x + 5y = 10

8) $y = ^2/_5x - 2$

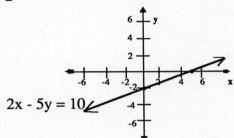

2x - 5y = 10

9) $y = -2x + 2$

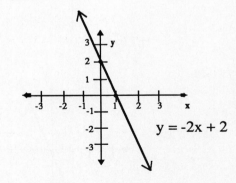

y = -2x + 2

10) $y = -^2/_3x - ^{17}/_3$

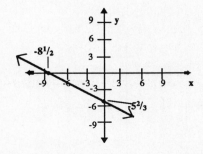

Section 7.3 Slope of a Line

The slope of a line is a ratio of the vertical change to the horizontal change between any two selected points on the line.

Slope of a Line through the Points (x_1, y_1) and (x_2, y_2)

Slope =

change in y (vertical change)/change in x (horizontal change) $= \frac{(y_2 - y_1)}{(x_2 - x_1)}$

It makes no difference which two points are selected when finding the slope of a line. It also makes no difference which point you label (x_1, y_1) or (x_2, y_2). The Greek capital letter delta, Δ is often used to represent the words "the change in" thus the slope, which is symbolized by the letter **m** is sometimes indicated as

$$\mathbf{m} = \frac{\Delta y}{\Delta x} = \frac{(y_2 - y_1)}{(x_2 - x_1)}$$

Example 1. Find the slope of the line through (-3, 7) and (1, 5).

Solution: We will designate the ordered pair (-3, 7) as (x_1, y_1) and the ordered pair (1,5) as (x_2, y_2).

$$\mathbf{m} = \frac{\Delta y}{\Delta x} = \frac{(y_2 - y_1)}{(x_2 - x_1)} = \frac{(5 - 7)}{[1 - (-3)]} = \frac{-2}{4} = -\frac{1}{2}$$

The slope is $-\frac{1}{2}$

If we had designated (1, 5) as (x_1, y_1) and (-3, 7) as (x_1, y_1), we would have obtained the same results.

$$\mathbf{m} = \frac{\Delta y}{\Delta x} = \frac{(y_2 - y_1)}{(x_2 - x_1)} = \frac{(7 - 5)}{[1 - (-3)]} = \frac{-2}{4} = -\frac{1}{2}$$

Summary:

A straight line where the value of y increases as x increases has a positive slope
A line with a positive slope rises as it moves from left to right.
A straight line where the value of y decreases as x increases has a negative slope.
A line with a negative slope falls as it moves from left to right.
A horizontal line has a slope of zero.
A vertical line has no slope.

Example 2   Consider the line illustrated in the figure below
(a) Determine its slope by observing the vertical change and horizontal change between the two given points.
(b) Calculate the slope of the line using the two given points.

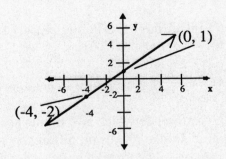

Solution: (a) The vertical change (y_2, y_1) is 3, and the horizontal change (x_2, x_1) is 4. The slope is $^3/_4$.

The slope is positive since the line rises from left to right.

(b) The ordered pairs indicated on the graph are (-4, -2) and (0,1). Now use the slope formula to calculate the slope. Using (0,1) as (x_1, y_1) and (-4,-2) as (x_2, y_2)

$$m = {}^{\Delta y}/_{\Delta x} = {}^{(y_2 - y_1)}/_{(x_2 - x_1)} = {}^{(-2 - 1)}/_{(-4 - 0)} = {}^{-3}/_{-4} = {}^3/_4$$

Example 3.   Find the slope of the line in the figure below by observing the vertical change and horizontal change between the two given points.

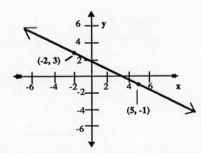

Solution: The vertical change (y_2, y_1) is 4, and thr horizontal change (x_2, x_1) is 7. The slope is $^{-4}/_7$ since the values of y decreases as the values of x increases.

$$m = {}^{\Delta y}/_{\Delta x} = {}^{(y_2 - y_1)}/_{(x_2 - x_1)} = {}^{[3 - (-1)]}/_{(-2 - 5)} = {}^4/_{-7} = {}^{-4}/_7$$

Exercises Set 7.3

Find the slope of the line through the given points
  1) (1, 4) and (5, 8)   2) (-5, -4) and (3, 6)
  3) (14, 2) and (2, -6)   4) (0,0) and (-5, 7)
  5) (0, 3) and (-3, 0)   6) (0, 2) and (-2, 1)

By observing the vertical and horizontal change of the line between the two points indicated, determine the slope of the line.

7)

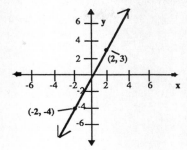

8)

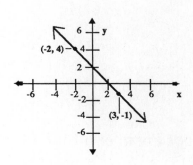

9)

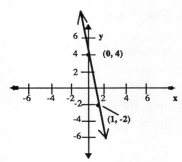

10)

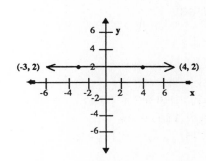

11)

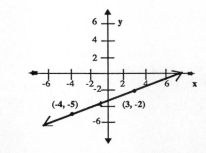

12)

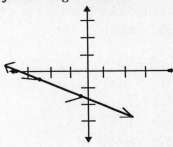

Answers for exercise set 7.3

1) 1   2) $^5/_4$
3) $^2/_3$ 4) $^{-7}/_5$
5) 1   6) $^1/_2$
7) $^7/_4$ 8) -1
9) -6   10) 0
11) $^3/_7$ 12) $^2/_4$

Section 7.4 Slope-Intercept Form of a Line

➡**Note:**   **Slope-Intercept Form of a Line**

$y = mx + b$ **m** represents the slope
                b represents the **y** intercept

To write an equation in slope-intercept form,
solve the equation for **y**.

Example 1.   Write the equation 3x - 4y = 8 in slope-intercept form. State the slope
and **y** intercept. Use the slope and the **y** intercept to draw the graph of
the equation.

Solution: Solve for **y**
                    3x - 4y = 8
              3x + (-3x) - 4y = 8 + (-3x)
                  0x - 4y = 8 + (-3x)
                    -4y = -3x + 8
                  $^{-4}/_{-4}y = ^{-3}/_{-4}x + ^8/_{-4}$
                    y = $^3/_4$x - 2

              slope = $^3/_4$ y intercept = (0, -2)

To graph the line, start
at the y intercept (0, -2). The
y intercept represents one
point on the line.

Find the other point
by applying a vertical change
of 3 and a horizontal change
of 4 from the y intercept.
Then draw the line connecting the two points.

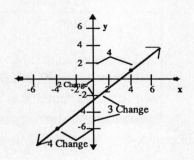

Example 2.   Determine the equation of the graph shown in the accompanying
graph.

Solution: In order to write the equation of the graph
you need to know the slope and the y intercept.

Find the slope. $m = \dfrac{(y_2 - y_1)}{(x_2 - x_1)}$

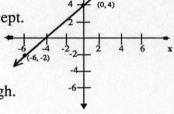

Use any two points that the line goes through.
The line goes through (-6, -2) and (0, 4).

$y_2 = 4$ $y_1 = -2$ $x_2 = 0$ $x_1 = -6$

$m = \dfrac{(y_2 - y_1)}{(x_2 - x_1)} = \dfrac{[(4) - (-2)]}{[(0) - (-6)]} = \dfrac{(4 + 2)}{(0 + 6)} = \dfrac{6}{6} = 1$

The slope m = 1.   The y intercept is 4.

$y = mx + b$
$y = 1x + 4$ ***Answer***

Summary:

> Linear Equations with the same slope are parallel lines.

Example 3.   Graph the following equations on the same set of axis.
$$y = \tfrac{1}{3}x + 4 \qquad y = \tfrac{1}{3}x - 3$$

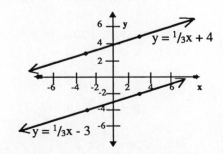

STANDARD FORM

Equations that can be put in the form **ax + by = c** where **a, b,** and **c** are constants, a and b are not both zero, and x and y are variables are called linear equations in Standard Form.

Example 4.   Write the following equations in **Standard Form.**
$$ax + by = c$$

a) $y = 3x - 2$ b) $5y + 2x = 7$ c) $5x = -8y + 23$

Solution   a) $y = 3x - 2$
                 $y - 3x = 3x - 3x - 2$
                 $y - 3x = -2$ ***Standard Form***

b) $5y + 2x = 7$
        $2x + 5y = 7$ ***Standard Form***

c) $5x = -8y + 23$
       $5x + 8y = -8y + 8y + 23$
       $5x + 8y = 23$
       $8y + 5x = 23$ ***Standard Form***

Example 5   Write the equation $2y - 3x = 8$ in (a) standard form, (b) slope-intercept form, and (c) point-slope form.

Solution: a) Standard form is $ax + by = c$
              $2y - 3x = 8$
             $-3x + 2y = 8$ ***Standard Form***

b) Slope-intercept form $y = mx + b$
            $2y - 3x = 8$
      $2y - 3x + 3x = 8 + 3x$
            $2y = 8 + 3x$
            $^{2y}/_2 = {^8}/_2 + {^{3x}}/_2$
            $y = 4 + {^{3x}}/_2$
            $y = {^{3x}}/_2 + 4$

The slope of the line is $^3/_2$ and the **y** intercept is 4.

c) Point-slope forms is $y - y_1 = m(x - x_1)$
        $y = {^{3x}}/_2 + 4$
      $y - 4 = {^{3x}}/_2 + 4 - 4$
      $y - 4 = {^{3x}}/_2$
      $y - 4 = {^3}/_2(x - 0)$

The slope of the line is $y = {^3}/_2$ and the point on the line is (0, 4)

Exercise Set 7.4

Determine the slope and y intercept, and graph the equation.
1) x + y = 7   2) 2x + y = 11
3) x = 6   4) 4y + x = 10
5) 5x - 4y = 8   6) y = -10

Determine the equation of each line.

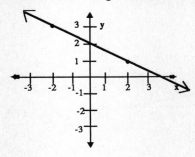
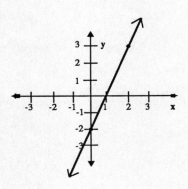

Determine if the two given lines are parallel.
9) y + 2x = 7   10) 3y + 6x = 15
   4y + 8x = -15   2y + x = 18

Answers for Exercise Set 7.4
1) Slope = -1   y intercept = 7

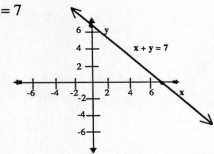

2) Slope = -2   y intercept = 11

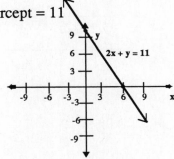

3) No slope   (vertical line)

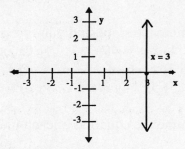

4) Slope = $-\frac{1}{4}$ y intercept = $2\frac{1}{2}$

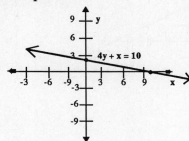

5) Slope = $\frac{5}{4}$ y intercept = -2

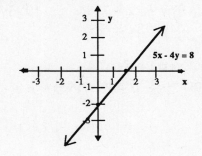

6) Slope = 0   y intercept = -10

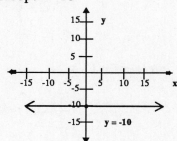

7) $y = -\frac{1}{2}x + 2$ 8) $y = \frac{5}{2}x - 2$

9) Yes   10) No

Section 7.5 Point-Slope Form of a Line

> **POINT-SLOPE FORM OF A LINE**
> $$y - y_1 = m(x - x_1)$$
>
> where **m** is the slope of the line and (x_1, y_1) is a point on the line.

Example 1.   Write an equation of the line that goes through the point (-1, -5) and has a slope of 2.

Solution: The slope **m** is 2. The point (-1, -5) is (x_1, y_1).
Substitute the appropriate values in the point-slope form of a line.

$m = 2 \quad x_1 = -1 \quad y_1 = -5$

$$
\begin{aligned}
y - y_1 &= m(x - x_1) \\
y - (-5) &= (2)[x - (-1)] \\
y + 5 &= 2(x + 1) \\
y + 5 &= 2x + 2 \\
y &= 2x - 3 \quad \textit{Answer}
\end{aligned}
$$

Example 2.   Write an equation of the line through the points (-2, 5) and (6, 5).

Solution: To use the point-slope form, you must first find the slope between the two points.

$y_2 = 5 \quad y_1 = 5 \quad x_2 = 6 \quad x_1 = -2$

$$m = \frac{(y_2 - y_1)}{(x_2 - x_1)} = \frac{(5 - 5)}{[6 - (-2)]} = \frac{0}{(6 + 2)} = \frac{0}{8} = 0$$

Use (-2, 5) or (6, 5) as (x_1, y_1)

$x_1 = -2 \qquad y_1 = 5 \qquad m = 0$

$$
\begin{aligned}
y - y_1 &= m(x - x_1) \\
y - (-5) &= (0)[x - (-2)] \\
y - 5 &= 0(x + 2) \\
y - 5 &= 0 \\
y &= 5 \qquad \textit{Answer}
\end{aligned}
$$

Exercise Set 7.5

Find the equation of a line with the properties given.
1) Slope = $^3/_2$, through (-1, 3)
2) Slope = -1, through (-2, 8)
3) Slope = -$^1/_3$, through (3, -4)
4) Through (-2, 1) and (3, 2)
5) Through (-2, 3) and (-1, 2)

6) Write the equation $3y = 4x - 15$ in standard form, slope-intercept form, and point-slope form.

7) Write the equation $-x = -2y + 8$ in standard form, slope-intercept form, and point-slope form.

8) Write the equation $-4x + y = 14$ in standard form, slope-intercept form, and point-slope form.

9) Write the equation $6y + 5x = 10$ in standard form, slope-intercept form, and point-slope form.

10) Write the equation $8y + 6x = 1$ in standard form, slope-intercept form, and point-slope form.

Answers for Exercise Set 7.5

1) $2y - 3x = 9$ 2) $x + y = 6$

3) $3y + x = -9$ 4) $5y - x = 7$

5) $y + x = 1$

6) $-4x + 3y = -15$ $y = ^4/_3x - 5$ $y + 5 = ^4/_3(x - 0)$

7) $x + 2y = 8$, $y = ^1/_2x + 4$ $y - 4 = ^1/_2(x + 0)$

8) $-4x + y = 14$, $y = 4x + 14$ $y - 14 = 4(x+0)$

9) $5x + 6y = 10$ $y = ^{-5}/_6x + ^{10}/_6$ $y - ^{10}/_6 = ^{-5}/_6(x + 0)$

10) $6x + 8y = 1$ $y = ^{-6}/_8x + ^1/_8$ $y - ^1/_8 = ^{-6}/_8(x+0)$

Section 7.6   Graphing Linear Inequalities
Summary:

> Replace the inequality symbol with an equal sign.
>
> Draw the graph of the equation in step 1. If the original inequality a ≥ or ≤ symbol, draw the graph using a solid line. If the original inequality contained a > or < symbol, draw the graph using a dashed line.
>
> Select any point not on the line and determine if this point is a solution to the inequality. If the selected point in a solution, shade the region on the side of the line containing this point. If the selected point does not satisfy the inequality, shade the region on the side of the line not containing this point.

Example 1.   Draw the graph of the inequality $2x - 3y < 6$.

Solution: Graph the inequality using the above outline.

(Step 1) $2x - 3y = 6$
                        $y = \frac{2}{3}x - 2$ Slope $= \frac{2}{3}$ y intercept $= -2$

(Step 2)   Since the inequality symbol
                     is < or > draw a broken line.

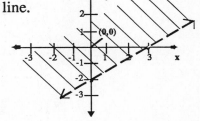

(Step 3) $(0, 0)$
                     $2x - 3y < 6$
                     $2(0) - 3(0) < 6$
                     $0 < 6$ *True*

Shade the side containing the point $(0, 0)$.

Exercise Set 7.6

Graph each inequality.
   1) $y < x + 1$ 2) $y > x$
   3) $x + y \geq 3$ 4) $2x + y \leq 4$
   5) $x < 2y + 6$ 6) $x + 2y > 0$
   7) $y < 2$ 8) $4x - 3y \geq 12$

Answers for Exercise Set 7.6

1)
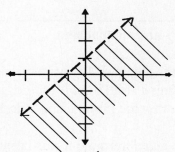

2)
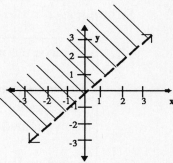

3)
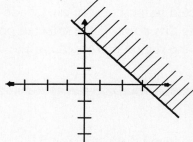

4)
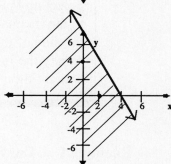

5)
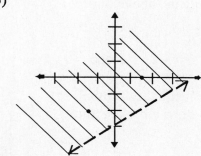

6)
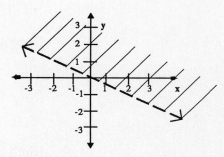

7)
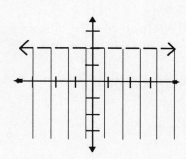

8)
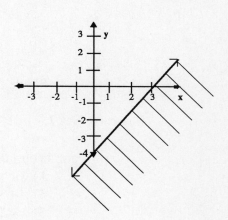

Practice Test Chapter 7

1) Determine which of the following ordered pairs satisfy the equation $y = 3x - 1$.

    a) $(1, 2)$ b) $(-1, -4)$ c) $(2, 3)$ d) $(1/3, 1)$

2) Find the slope and y intercept of $5x + 2y = -3$.

3) Write an equation of the graph in the accompanying figure.

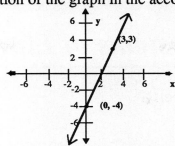

4) Write an equation of the line with a slope of $-\frac{7}{12}$ passing through the point (-1, 1).

5) Write an equation of the line passing through the points (1, 3) and (-8, -10).

Graph the following.

6) $3y - 2x = 0$ 7) $y = 2x + 3$

8) $x = 15$ 9) $3x + 2y = 8$

10) $x + y \leq 2$

Answers for Practice Test Chapter 7

1. a) yes   b) yes   c) no   d) no

2) Slope = $-\frac{5}{2}$ y intercept = $-\frac{3}{2}$

3) $y = \frac{7}{3}x - 4$

4) $7x + 12y = 5$ 5) $9y - 13x = 14$

6)

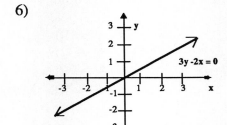

7)

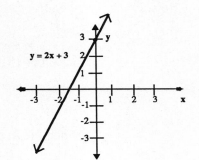

8)

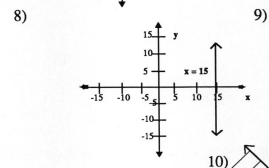

9)

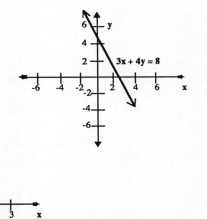

10)

Chapter 8   Systems of Linear Equations

Section 8.1 Introduction

Summary:

System of Linear Equations or Simultaneous linear equations consists of two or more linear equations. Solving a system of Linear Equations means find a common solution.

Example 1.   Determine which of the following ordered pairs satisfy the system of equations.

$$x + y = 2$$
$$3x - y = 10$$

a) (-1, 3)   b) (3, -1)   c) (1, -7)

Satisfy the system of equations means that the ordered pair has to be true in both equations.

Solution: a) Substitute -1 for x and 3 for y in each equation.

$x + y = 2$	$3x - y = 10$
$(-1) + (3) = 2$	$3(-1) - (3) = 10$
$2 = 2$ *True*	$-3 - 3 = 10$
	$-6 = 10$ *False*

Since (1, 3) does not satisfy both equations, it is not a solution.

Solution: b) Substitute 3 for x and -1 for y in each equation.

$x + y = 2$	$3x - y = 10$
$(3) + (-1) = 2$	$3(?) - (?) = 10$
$(?) = 2$ *True*	$9 - (-1) = 10$
	$10 = 10$ True

Since (3, -1) satisfies both equations, it is a solution to the system of linear equations.

Solution: c) Substitute 1 for x and -7 for y in each equation.

$$x + y = 2 \qquad\qquad 3x - y = 10$$
$$(?) + (?) = 2 \qquad\qquad 3(1) - (-7) = 10$$
$$-6 = 2 \quad \textit{False} \qquad 3 + 7 = 10$$
$$10 = 10 \quad \textit{True}$$

Since (1, -7) does not satisfy both equations, it is not a solution.

Answers for (?) in Example 1.   b) 2, 3, -1   c) 1, -7

Exercise Set 8.1

Determine which, if any, of the following ordered pairs satisfy each system of linear equations.

1)   x + 2y = 4
        x + 4y = 10

a) (-2, 3)   b) (2, 1)   c) (2, 2)

2)   x - y = 1
        x + y = 5

a) (5, 4)   b) (4, 1)   c) (3, 2)

3)   2x + y = 2
        6x - y = 22

a) (2, -10)   b) (3, -4)   c)(1, 0)

4)   3x + 4y = 14
        2x + y = 6

a) (1, 4)   b) (2, 2)   c) (4, $^1/_2$)

5)   x = 6
        2x - y = 3

a) (6, 0)   b) (2, 1)   c) (6, 9)

Answers for Exercise Set 8.1

1) (-2, 3)   2) (3, 2)

3) (3, -4)   4) (2, 2)   5) (6, 9)

Section 8.2 Solving Systems of Equations Graphically

Summary:

To obtain the solution to a system of equations graphically, graph each equation and determine the point or points of intersection.

If one point is common to both equations, the system of linear equations is consistent.

If no points are common to both equations, the system of linear equations is inconsistent.

If a system of linear equations is inconsistent, then the linear equations have the same slope.

If an infinite number of points are common to both equations, the system of linear equations is dependent.

If a system of linear equations is dependent, then one equation is a multiple of the other equation.

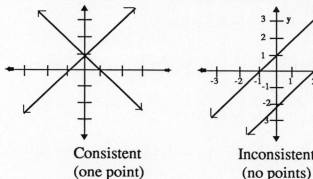

| Consistent (one point) | Inconsistent (no points) | Dependent (Infinite number of points) |

Example 1. Solve the following system of equations graphically.

$$x + y = 2$$
$$2y - 5x = -10$$

Solution: Solve each equation for y and graph using the slope and y intercept.

$$x + y = 2$$
$$y = -x + 2$$
slope = -1   y intercept = 2

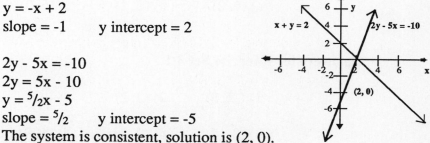

$$2y - 5x = -10$$
$$2y = 5x - 10$$
$$y = {}^5/_2 x - 5$$
slope = ${}^5/_2$ y intercept = -5

The system is consistent, solution is (2, 0).

Check: Substitute 2 for x and 0 for y in both equations.

$$x + y = 2 \qquad\qquad 2y - 5x = -10$$
$$(2) + (0) = 2 \qquad\qquad 2(0) - 5(2) = -10$$
$$2 = 2 \quad \textit{True} \qquad\qquad 0 - 10 = -10$$
$$-10 = -10 \quad \textit{True}$$

Exercise Set 8.2

Identify each system of linear equations as **consistent, inconsistent, or dependent.**

State whether the system has exactly **one solution, no solution, or an infinite number of solutions.**

1)
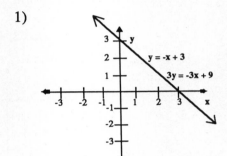

2)
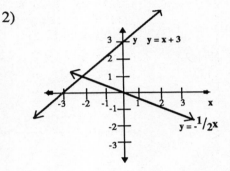

3)
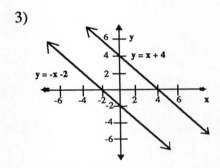

Express each equation in slope-intercept form, without graphing the equations.

State whether the system of equations has exactly one solution, no solution, or an infinite number of solutions.

4) $x + y = 4$ 5) $5x + 3y = 17$ 6) $x - 2y = 2$
     $2x = 6 - 2y$ $x + 3y = 1$ $2x = 4y + 4$

Determine the solution of each system of equations graphically.

7) $2x + 3y = 6$ 8) $x = 2$
     $5x + 3y = 6$ $y = 4$

9) $y = 3 - 2x$ 10) $2y = x - 4$
     $y + 2x = 0$ $x + 4y = 4$

Answers for Exercise Set 8.2

1) Dependent and has an infinite number of solutions.

2) Consistent and has one solution.

3) Inconsistent and has no solutions.

4) $y = -x + 4$
      $y = -x + 3$ Inconsistent with no solutions.

5) $y = -\frac{5}{3}x + \frac{17}{3}$
      $y = -\frac{1}{3}x + \frac{1}{3}$ Consistent with one solution.

6) $y = \frac{1}{2}x - 1$
      $y = \frac{1}{2}x - 1$ Dependent with an infinite number of solutions.

7)   Solution (0, 2)

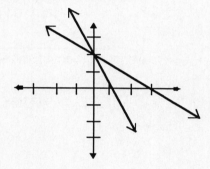

8)   Solution (2, 4)

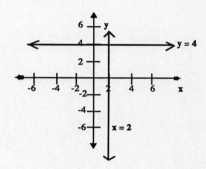

9)   No Solution

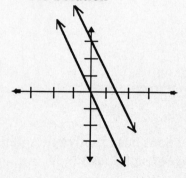

10)   Solution (4, 0)

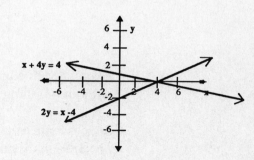

Section 8.3 Solving Systems of Equations by Substitution.

Summary:

To Solve a System of Equations by Substitution

1. Solve for a variable in either equation. (If possible solve for a variable with numerical coefficient of 1 to avoid working with fractions.)

2. Substitute the expression found for the variable in step 1 into the other equation.

3. Solve the equation determined in step 2 to find the value of one variable.

4. Substitute the value found in step 3 into the equation obtained in step 1 to find the remaining variable.

Example 1.   Solve the following system of equations by substitution.

$$x + y = 2$$
$$2y - 5x = -10$$

Solution:

(Step 1)   Solve for x in $x + y = 2$.
$$x + y = 2$$
$$x = -y + 2$$

(Step 2)   Now substitute $(-y + 2)$ for x in the other equation.
$$2y - 5x = -10$$
$$2y - 5(-y + 2) = -10$$

(Step 3)
$$2y + 5y - 10 = -10$$
$$7y - 10 = -10$$
$$y = 0$$
$$7y = 0$$

(Step 4)   Now substitute 0 in for y in the equation $x = -y + 2$.
$$x = -(0) + 2$$
$$x = 2$$

The solution to the system is $(2, 0)$.

Check: $x + y = 2$ $(2) + (0) = 2$
$$2 = 2 \quad \textbf{\textit{True}}$$

$$2y - 5x = -10 \qquad 2(0) - 5(2) = -10$$
$$0 - 10 = -10$$
$$-10 = -10 \quad \textbf{\textit{True}}$$

Example 2. Solve the following system of equations by substitution.

$$y = 3 - 2x$$
$$y + 2x = 0$$

Solution:

(Step 1) Since the equation $y = 3 - 2x$ is already solved for one variable, no other operations need to be performed.

(Step 2) Substitute $(3 - 2x)$ for y in $y + 2x = 0$.

$$(3 - 2x) + 2x = 0$$

(Step 3)
$$3 - 2x + 2x = 0$$
$$3 = 0 \quad \textit{False}$$

Since the statement $3 = 0$ is false, the system has no solution. (Therefore, the lines will be parallel and the system is inconsistent.

Example 3. Solve the following system of equations by substitution.

$$x - 2y = 2$$
$$2x = 4y + 4$$

Solution:

(Step 1) Solve $x - 2y = 2$ for x.
$$x - 2y = 2$$
$$x = 2y + 2$$

(Step 2) Substitute $(2y + 2)$ for x in $2x = 4y + 4$.
$$2(2y + 2) = 4y + 4$$

(Step 3)
$$4y + 4 = 4y + 4$$
$$4 = 4$$

Since the statement $4 = 4$ is always true, this system has an infinite number of solutions. (Therefore, the lines will be the same when graphed and the system is dependent.)

Exercise Set 8.3

Find the solution to each system of equations using substitution.

1) $3x + y = 8$
$2x - 3y = -13$

2) $2x - 3y = 4$
$3x + y = 17$

3) $x + 3y = 7$
$2x - 7y = 1$

4) $3x - 4y = 1$
$x + 5y = 13$

5) $2x + y = 2$
$4x - y = 1$

6) $4x - 14 = 2y$
$2x - 3y = 5$

7) $2x - 13y = 45$
$5x - 10y = 45$

8) $5x - 4y = 5$
$7x - 5y = 4$

Answers for Exercise Set 8.3

1) (1, 5)	2) (5, 2)
3) (4, 1)	4) (3, 2)
5) ($^1/_2$, 1)	6) (4, 1)
7) (3, -3)	8) (-3, -5)

Section 8.4 Solving Systems of Equations by the Addition Method.

Summary:

To Solve a System of Equations by the Addition (or Elimination) Method:

1) If necessary, rewrite each equation so that the terms containing variables appear on the left side of the equal sign and any constants appear on the right side of the equal sign.

2) If necessary, multiply one or both equations by a constant(s) so that when the equations are added the resulting sum will contain only one variable.

3) Add the equations. This will result in a single equation containing only one variable.

4) Solve for the variable in the equation in step 3.

5) Substitute the value found in step 4 into either of the original equations. Solve that equation to find the value of the remaining variable.

Example 1.　Solve the following system of equations using the addition method.
$$3x + 5y = 13$$
$$12x - 5y = 2$$

Solution:　Skip steps 1 and 2 since the requirements have already been satisfied.

(Step 3)
$$3x + 5y = 13$$
$$\underline{12x - 5y = 2}$$
$$15x + 0y = 15$$

(Step 4)
$$15x = 15$$
$$x = 1$$

(Step 5) Substitute 1 for x in 3x + 5y = 13.

$$3(1) + 5y = 13$$
$$3 + 5y = 13$$
$$5y = 10$$
$$y = 2$$

The solution is (1, 2).

Example 2. Solve the fol lowing system of equations using the addition method.

$$x = -8y + 35$$
$$-y = -2x + 2$$

Solution:

(Step l) $x = -8y + 35$ $-y = -2x + 2$
            $x + 8y = 35$ $2x - y = 2$

(Step 2) $x + 8y = 35$
            $2x - y = 2$

The variable **x** can be eliminated by multiplying the first equation by (-2).

$$-2[x + 8y = 35] \text{ gives } -2x - 16y = -70$$
$$2x - y = 2 \qquad\qquad 2x - y = 2$$

(Step 3) $-2x - 16y = -70$
          $\underline{2x - y = 2}$
          $0x - 17y = -68$

(Step 4) $-17y = -68$
            $y = \mathbf{4}$

(Step 5)   Substitute 4 for y in $2x - y = 2$.
                           $2x - (4) = 2$
                           $2x = 6$
                           $\mathbf{x = 3}$

The solution is (3, 4).

Example 3. Solve the following system of equations using the addition method:

$$y = -x + 3$$
$$x + y = 4$$

Solution:

(Step l) $y = -x + 3$
            $y + x = 3$
(Step 2) $x + y = 3$
            $x + y = 4$

The variable x can be eliminated by multiplying the first equation by (-1).

$$(-1)[x + y = 3] \quad \text{gives} \quad -x - y = -3$$
$$x + y = 4 \qquad\qquad x + y = 4$$

(Step 3)
$$-x - y = -3$$
$$\underline{x + y = 4}$$
$$0x + 0y = 1$$

Since $0 = 1$ is a false statement, this system has no solution.
The system is inconsistent and the lines will be parallel when graphed.

Example 4. Solve the following system of equations using the addition method.
$$x - 2y = 2$$
$$2x = 4y + 4$$

Solution:

(Step 1) $\quad 2x = 4y + 4$
$$2x - 4y = 4$$

(Step 2) $x - 2y = 2$
$$2x - 4y = 4$$
The **x** variable can be eliminated by multiplying the first equation by (-2).

$$-2[x - 2y = 2] \quad \text{gives} \quad -2x + 4y = -4$$
$$2x - 4y = 4 \qquad\qquad 2x - 4y = 4$$

(Step 3)
$$-2x + 4y = -4$$
$$\underline{2x - 4y = 4}$$
$$0 = 0$$

Since $0 = 0$ is a true statement, the system is dependent and has an infinite number of solutions.

Exercise Set 8.4
Solve each system of equations using the addition method.

1) $\quad 3x - 2y = 8$
$\quad 3x + 5y = -41$

2) $\quad 3x - 4y = -2$
$\quad x + 2y = 6$

3) $\quad 5x - y = 2$
$\quad x - y = -2$

4) $\quad x + 8y = 35$
$\quad 2x - y = 2$

5) $\quad 2x - 5y = -2$
$\quad 5y - 2x = 10$

6) $\quad 3x - 5y = -9$
$\quad 6x - 7y = -9$

7) $\quad 3y + 9x = 12$
$\quad 3x + y = 4$

8) $\quad 4x - 21y = 11$
$\quad 6x - 17y = 31$

Answers to Exercise Set 8.4

1) (-2, -7)   2) (2, 2)
3) (1, 3)   4) (3, 4)
5) No solution   6) (2, 3)
7) Dependent   8) (8, 1)

Section 8.5 Applications of Systems of Equations

Example 1.   One positive number is twice another. The larger is 10 more than the smaller. Find the numbers.

Solution: **Let x** = the smaller number   **Let y** = the larger number

Statement	*Equation*
One positive number is twice another.	$y = 2x$
The larger is 10 more than the smaller.	$y = x + 10$

system of equations $y = 2x$
$y - x = 10$

Substitute 2x for y in $y - x = 10$
$(2x) - x = 10$
$x = 10$

Substitute 10 for x in $y = 2x$
$y = 2(10)$
$y = 20$

The smaller number x is 10 and the larger number y is 20.

Example 2.   In his bank, Bill Hontz has three times as many quarters as nickels. If the value of the quarters is $5.60 more than the value of the nickels, how many of each kind does he have?

Solution: **Let q** = quarters   **Let n** = nickels

Statement	*Equation*
Three times as many quarters as nickels.	$q = 3n$
The value of quarters is $5.60 more than the value of the nickels.	$25q = 5n + 560$

system of equations $q = 3n$
$25q = 5n + 560$

Substitute 3n for q in $\quad 25q = 5n + 560$

$$25(3n) = 5n + 560$$
$$75n = 5n + 560$$
$$70n = 560$$
$$\mathbf{n = 8}$$

Substitute 8 for n in q = 3n

$$q = 3(8)$$
$$\mathbf{q = 24}$$

Bill Hontz has 8 nickels and 24 quarters.

Example 3. Two planes leave the airport at the same time and fly in opposite directions. The speed of the faster plane is 100 m.p.h. faster than the slower one. At the end of 5 hours, they are 2000 miles apart. Find the rate of each plane.

Solution: **Let x** = speed of the fast plane   **Let y** = speed of the slow plane

Statement	*Equation*
The speed of the faster plane is 100 m.p.h. faster than the slower one.	$x = y + 100$
At the end of 5 hours, they are 2000 miles apart.	$5x + 5y = 2000$

(Rate x Time = Distance)

system of equations $\quad \mathbf{x = y + 100} \qquad or \qquad \mathbf{x - y = 100}$
$$\qquad\qquad\qquad\qquad \mathbf{5x + 5y = 2000} \qquad\qquad \mathbf{5x + 5y = 2000}$$

The **y** variable can be eliminated by multiplying the first equation by 5.

$5[x - y = 100]$ $\qquad$ gives $\qquad$ $5x - 5y = 500$
$5x + 5y = 2000$ $\qquad\qquad\qquad\qquad$ $5x + 5y = 2000$

Add $\qquad\qquad 5x - 5y \;= 500$
$$\qquad\qquad\quad \underline{5x + 5y \;= 2000}$$
$$\qquad\qquad 10x \qquad = 2500$$
$$\qquad\qquad\quad x \qquad = 250$$

Substitute 250 for $\;$ x in $\qquad$ x = y + 100
$$\qquad\qquad\qquad\qquad\qquad 250 = y + 100$$
$$\qquad\qquad\qquad\qquad\qquad \mathbf{150 = y}$$

The speed of the fast plane is 250 m.p.h. and the speed of the slow plane is 150 m.p.h.

Example 4. Don Rhine invested a total of $4000. One part of which he earned 4%. On the remainder he lost 3%. Combining his earnings and losses, he found his annual income to be $55. Find the amounts at each rate.

Solution: **Let x** = 1st investment   **Let y** = 2nd investment

system of equations $x + y = 4000$ *or* $x + y = 4000$
                        $.04x - .03y = 55$ $4x \quad 3y = 5500$

The y variable can be eliminated by multiplying the first equation by 3.

$$3[x + y = 4000] \quad \text{gives} \quad 3x + 3y = 12000$$
$$4x - 3y = 5500 \quad \text{gives} \quad 4x - 3y = 5500$$

Add $3x + 3y = 12000$
        $\underline{4x - 3y = 5500}$
        $7x \qquad = 17500$
        $x \qquad = 2500$

Substitute 2500 for x in $x + y = 4000$
                        $2500 + y = 4000$
                        $y = 1500$

Don Rhine invested $2500 at 4% profit and $1500 at 3% loss.

Exercise Set 8.5

In each problem (a) express the problem as a system of linear equations, and (b) use the method of your choice to find the solution to the problem.

1) The sum of two numbers is 50 and their difference is 4. Find the numbers.

2) The sum of the number of teeth on two gears is 64, and their difference is 12. How many teeth are on each gear?

3) Two trains leave the Buffalo terminal at the same time and travel in opposite directions. After 8 hours they are 360 miles apart. The speed of the faster train is 3 m.p.h. less than twice that of the slower train. Find the rate of each train.

4) A boat can travel 24 miles downstream in 2 hours and 16 miles upstream in the same length of time. What is the speed of the boat in still water and what is the speed of the current?

5) Gallo's Clothing Store sells suits at $125 and $185 each. The store owners observe that they sold 40 suits for a total of $5,720. How many suits of each type did they sell?

6) Toni Parlave has $2.40 in dimes and nickels. If the total number of coins is 30, how many dimes and nickels does he have?

7) Gary has $20,000, part of which he invests at 8% interest and the rest at 6%. If his total income from the two investments was $1,460, how much did he invest at each rate?

8) Paul Arends has $18,000 to invest, part at 10% interest and the remainder at 8%. If his income from each investment was the same, what does he invest at each rate?

9) A 12 foot board is cut into two pieces so that one piece is 4 feet longer than the other. How long is each piece?

10) A 24 foot cable is cut into two pieces so that one piece is twice as long as the other. How long is each piece?

Answers for Exercise Set 8.5

1) $x + y = 50$
$x - y = 4$

23, 27

2) $x + y = 64$
$x - y = 12$

26, 38

3) $8x + 8y = 360$
$x - 2y = 3$

14, 31

4) $2x - 2y = 16$
$2x + 2y = 24$

2 m. p. h. (current)
10 m.p.h. (boat speed)

5) $x + y = 40$
$125x + 185y = 5720$

12 at $185 each
28 at $125 each

6) $x + y = 30$
$5x + 10y = 240$

12 nickels
18 dimes

7) $x + y = 20,000$
$.08x + .06y = 1460$

$ 7 ,000 at   6%
$13,000 at   8%

8) $x + y = 18,000$
$.10x = .08y$

$ 8 ,000 at   10%
$10,000 at   8%

9) $x + y = 12$
$x - y = 4$

4, 8

10) $x + y = 24$
$x = 2y$

8, 16

Section 8.6 Systems of Linear Inequalities (Optional)

Summary:

> To Solve a System of Linear Inequalities:
>
> Graph each inequality on the same set of axes. The solution is the set of points that satisfy all the inequalities in the system. The solution is all the points in the intersection of the two shaded regions.

Example 1.   Determine the solution to the system of inequalities.

$$y > x + 2$$
$$y < -x + 4$$

Solution: First graph $y > x + 2$. Now on the same set of axes, graph the inequality $y < -2x + 4$. The solution labeled **S** is the part of the graph where the two shaded regions intersect. All the points in region **S** will satisfy both inequalities.

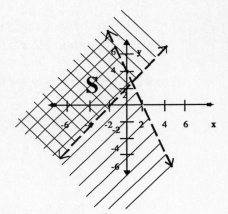

Example 2.   Determine the solution to the system of inequalities.

$$x < -2$$
$$y < -x$$

Solution: First graph $x < -2$. Now on the same set of axes, graph $y < -x$. The solution to the system is the region of intersection labeled **S**.

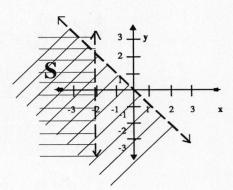

Exercise Set 8.6

Determine the solution to each system of inequalities.

1) $x + y < 3$
     $y < x - 2$

2) $y > \frac{1}{2}x$
     $y > -x + 2$

3) $y \leq x$
     $v \leq 2$

4) $y < x + 1$
     $2x + y \leq 4$

5)   y > x
       x + y ≥ 3
	6) x < 2y + 6
	       x + 2y > 0

Answers for Exercise Set 8.6

1)
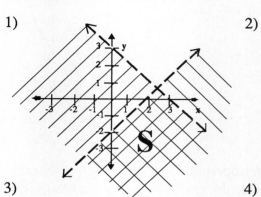

2)
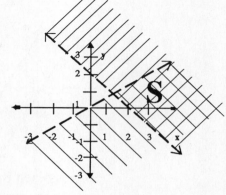

3)
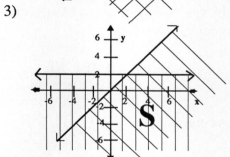

4)
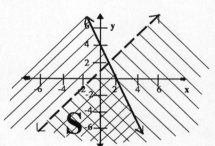

5)
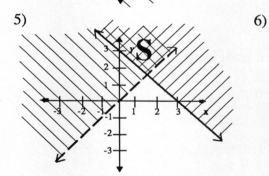

6)
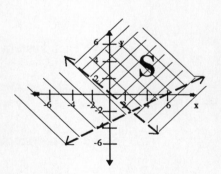

Practice Test Chapter 8

1) Determine which, if any, of the ordered pairs satisfy the system of equations.

$$2 - 3y = 6$$
$$x - y = 1$$

a) (-3 , -4)　　 b) (4 , 3)　　 c) (3 , 0)

Identify each system as consistent, inconsistent, or dependent. State whether the system has exactly one solution, no solutions, or an infinite number of solutions.

2)

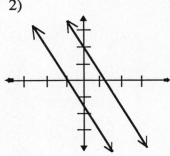

3)

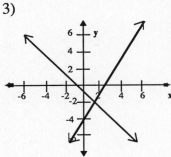

Express each equation in slope-intercept form. Then determine, without solving the system, whether the system of equations has exactly one solution, no solution, or an infinite number of solutions.

4)   x + 2y = 7   5)   x + 5y = 10
       3x + 6y = 15   2x = -10y + 20

Solve each system of equations graphically.

6)   3x + 4y = 12   7)   3x + 4y = -6
       4y + 7x = 12   y = 3 - 3x

Solve each system of equations using substitution.

8)   2y - 3x = 6   9)   5x + 3y = 6
       y = 3 - 2x   2x + 3y = -3

Solve each system of equations using the addition method.

10)   7x + y = 42   11)   4x - 2y = -14
       3x - y = 8   4x - 5y = -32

Express the problem as a system of linear equations, and use the method of your choice to find the solution to the problem.

12) Dave Hopkins and Joe Nacca together eat 8 chocolate doughnuts. If twice the number Joe eats is the same as the number Dave eats plus one, how many does each person eat?

Answers for Practice Test Chapter 8

1) a   2) Inconsistent
                 No solution

3) Consistent
   One solution

4) $y = -\frac{1}{2}x + 7$, Inconsistent
   $y = -\frac{1}{2}x + \frac{15}{6}$, No solution

5) $y = -\frac{1}{5}x + 2$, Dependent
   $y = -\frac{1}{5}x + 2$, Infinite number of solutions

6) Solution (0 , 3)

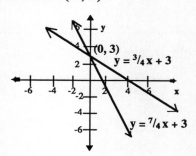

7) Solution (2 , -3)

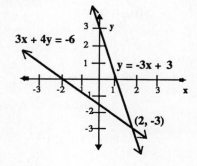

8)   (0 , 3)   9)   (3 , -3)
10) (5 , 7)   11) ($-\frac{1}{2}$, 6)

12) 5 doughnuts for Dave, 3 doughnuts for Joe

Chapter 9 Roots and Radicals

Section 9.1 Introduction

Summary:

$\sqrt{x}$ is read "the square root of x"

Radical Expression $\overset{\text{RADICAL SIGN}}{\sqrt{x}}$

$\underset{\text{ROOT INDEX}}{\overset{\text{RADICAND}}{}}$

$\sqrt{x}$ means $\sqrt[2]{x}$

If the index of the root is not written, square root is implied.

The principal or positive square root of a real number x, written $\sqrt{x}$, is that positive number whose square equals x.

The negative square root of a positive real number x, written $-\sqrt{x}$ is -x.

Square roots of negative numbers are not real numbers and therefore, do not exist within the scope of this course.

Example 1.   Evaluate

a) $\sqrt{16}$ b) $\sqrt{144}$ c) $\sqrt{16/25}$ d) $\sqrt{100/169}$

Solution: a) $\sqrt{16}$ $= 4$ since $4^2 = (4)(4) = 16$

b) $\sqrt{144}$ $= 12$ since $12^2 = (12)(12) = 144$

c) $\sqrt{16/25}$ $= {}^4/_5$ since $({}^4/_5)^2 = {}^4/_5 \cdot {}^4/_5 = {}^{16}/_{25}$

d) $\sqrt{100/169}$ $= {}^{10}/_{13}$ since $({}^{10}/_{13})^2 = {}^{10}/_{13} \cdot {}^{10}/_{13} = {}^{100}/_{169}$

Example 2.   Evaluate
a) $- \sqrt{16}$ b) $- \sqrt{144}$ c) $- \sqrt{16/25}$

Solution: a) $- \sqrt{16}$ $= -4$ since $(-4)^2 = (-4)(-4) = 16$

b) $- \sqrt{144}$ $= -12$ since $(-12)^2 = (-12)(-12) = 144$

c) $- \sqrt{16/25}$ $= -{}^4/_5$ since $(-{}^4/_5)^2 = -{}^4/_5 \cdot -{}^4/_5 = {}^{16}/_{25}$

Change Square Root to Exponential Form

$$\sqrt{\boxed{}} = \boxed{}^{1/2}\text{--Index of square root}$$

Radicand

Example 3   Write each radical in exponential form.
a) $\sqrt{69}$ b) $\sqrt{13x}$

Solution   a) $69^{1/2}$ b) $(13x)^{1/2}$

Excercise Set 9.1

Evaluate each expression.

1) $\sqrt{36}$ 2) $-\sqrt{4}$

3) $\sqrt{144/225}$ 4) $-\sqrt{81}$

5) $\sqrt{64}$ 6) $\sqrt{49}$

7) $\sqrt{64/100}$ 8) $\sqrt{225}$

9) $\sqrt{25}$ 10) $-\sqrt{121}$

Use Appendix B on your calculator to evaluate each expression.

11) $\sqrt{7}$ 12) $-\sqrt{12}$

13) $\sqrt{3}$ 14) $\sqrt{2}$

15) $-\sqrt{5}$ 16) $\sqrt{19}$

Write each of the following in exponential form.

17) $\sqrt{7}$ 18) $\sqrt{3xy}$

19) $\sqrt{37x^5}$ 20) $\sqrt{19z^3}$

Answers for Exercise Set 9.1

1) 6   2) -2   3) $^{12}/_{15}$

4) -9   5) 8   6) 7

7) $-^8/_{10}$ 8) 15   9) 5

10) -11   11) 2.6458   12) -3.4641

13) 1.7321   14) 1.4142   15) 2.2361

16) 4.3589   17) $7^{1}/_2$ 18) $(3xy)^{1/2}$

19) $(37x^5)^{1/2}$ 20) $(19z^3)^{1/2}$

Section 9.2 Multiplying and Simplifying Square Roots

Summary:

Product Rule for Radicals
$$\sqrt{a} \cdot \sqrt{b} = \sqrt{a \cdot b} \qquad a \geq 0, b \geq 0$$

To Simplify a Square Root Containing Only a Numerical Value

1) Write the numerical value as a product of the largest perfect square factor and another factor.

2) Use the product rule to write the expression as a product of square roots of the factors.

3) Find the square root of the perfect square factor.

Example 1. Simplify $\sqrt{12}$

Solution: The only perfect square factor of 12 is 4.
$$\sqrt{12} = \sqrt{4 \cdot 3}$$
$$= \sqrt{4} \cdot \sqrt{3}$$
$$= 2\sqrt{3}$$

Example 2. Simplify $\sqrt{72}$

Solution: The only perfect square factor of 72 is 36.
$$\sqrt{72} = \sqrt{36 \cdot 2}$$
$$= \sqrt{36} \cdot \sqrt{2}$$
$$= (?)\sqrt{2}$$

Answer to (?) in Example 2. $6\sqrt{2}$

Summary:

> Evaluate the square root of a radicand containing a variable raised to an even number.
>
> $$\sqrt{a^{2 \cdot n}} = a^n \qquad\qquad a > 0$$
>
> A variable raised to an even power equals the variable raised to one-half that power.

Example 3. Simplify
  a) $\sqrt{x^{14}}$ b) $\sqrt{x^4 y^{19}}$ c) $\sqrt{w^6 z^{20}}$

Solution:

  a) $\sqrt{x^{14}} = x^7$ since $(x^7)^2 = x^{14}$

  b) $\sqrt{x^4 y^{10}} = x^2 y^5$ since $(x^2 y^5)^2 = x^4 y^{10}$

  c) $\sqrt{w^6 z^{20}} = w^3 z^{10}$ since $(w^3 z^{10})^2 = w^6 z^{20}$

Summary:

> **To evaluate the square root of a radicand containing a variable raised to an odd power.**
>
> 1) Express the variable as the product of two factors, one of which has an exponent of 1 (the other will therefore be a perfect square factor).
>
> 2) Use the product rule to simplify.

Example 4. Simplify
  a) $\sqrt{w^{13}}$ b) $\sqrt{x^7}$ c) $\sqrt{x^3 y^{10}}$

Solution: a) $\sqrt{w^{13}} = \sqrt{w^{12} \cdot w} = \sqrt{w^{12}} \cdot \sqrt{w} = w^6 \sqrt{w}$

  b) $\sqrt{x^7} = \sqrt{x^6 \cdot x} = \sqrt{x^6} \cdot \sqrt{x} = x^3 \sqrt{x}$

  c) $\sqrt{x^3 y^{10}} = \sqrt{x^2 \cdot x \cdot y^{10}} = \sqrt{x^2 y^{10}} \cdot \sqrt{x} = x y^5 \sqrt{x}$

Example 5. Simplify
  a) $\sqrt{16 w^3}$ b) $\sqrt{8 x^7}$ c) $\sqrt{32 x^{10} y^7}$

Solution: a) $\sqrt{16 w^3} = \sqrt{16 w^2 \cdot w} = \sqrt{16 w^2} \cdot \sqrt{w} = 4 w \sqrt{w}$

b) $\sqrt{8x^7} = \sqrt{4 \cdot 2 \cdot x^6 \cdot x} = \sqrt{4x^6} \cdot \sqrt{2x} = 2x^3\sqrt{2x}$

c) $\sqrt{32x^{10}y^7} = \sqrt{16 \cdot 2 \cdot x^{10} \cdot y^6 \cdot y} = \sqrt{16x^{10}y^6} = \sqrt{2y} = 4x^5y^3\sqrt{2y}$

➡**Note:** The radicand of your simplified answer should not contain any perfect square factors or variables with an exponent higher than 1.

Example 6. Multiply and simplify where possible.
a) $\sqrt{6} \cdot \sqrt{3}$ b) $\sqrt{27} \cdot \sqrt{3}$ c) $\sqrt{1/2x} \cdot \sqrt{18x}$

Solution: a) $\sqrt{6} \cdot \sqrt{3} = \sqrt{18} = \sqrt{9 \cdot 2} = \sqrt{9} \cdot \sqrt{2} = 3\sqrt{2}$

b) $\sqrt{27} \cdot \sqrt{3} = \sqrt{81} = 9$

c) $\sqrt{1/2x} \cdot \sqrt{18x} = \sqrt{9x^2} = 3x$

Exercise Set 9.2

Simplify each expression.

1) $\sqrt{100}$ 2) $-\sqrt{49}$ 3) $\sqrt{49/121}$ $\sqrt{x^5}$

4) $\sqrt{45}$ 5) $\sqrt{72}$ 6) $-\sqrt{500}$

7) $\sqrt{x^3}$ 8) $\sqrt{x^2y}$ 9) $\sqrt{64x^2d}$

10) $\sqrt{8x^3y^5}$ 11) $\sqrt{75b^3d^{10}}$ 12) $\sqrt{169w^7z^{11}}$

Simplify each expression.

13) $\sqrt{10} \cdot \sqrt{5}$ 14) $\sqrt{40} \cdot \sqrt{5}$

15) $\sqrt{3b} \cdot \sqrt{12b^4}$ 16) $\sqrt{4x} \cdot \sqrt{xy}$

17) $\sqrt{5a^3b} \cdot \sqrt{10b}$ 18) $\sqrt{4c^3d} \cdot \sqrt{6cd^2}$

19) $\sqrt{5ab} \cdot \sqrt{2a}$ 20) $\sqrt{5c} \cdot \sqrt{5c}$

Answers for Exercise Set 9.2

1) 10   2) -7   3) $7/11$ 4) $3\sqrt{5}$

5) $6\sqrt{2}$ 6) $-10\sqrt{5}$ 7) $x\sqrt{x}$ 8) $x\sqrt{y}$

9) $8x\sqrt{d}$ 10) $2xy^2\sqrt{2xy}$ 11) $5bd^5\sqrt{3}$ 12) $13w^3z^5\sqrt{wz}$

13) $5\sqrt{2}$ 14) $10\sqrt{2}$ 15) $6b^2\sqrt{b}$ 16) $2x\sqrt{y}$

17) $5ab\sqrt{2a}$ 18) $2c^2d\sqrt{6d}$ 19) $a\sqrt{10b}$ 20) $5c$

Section 9.3 Dividing and Simplifying Radicals

Summary:

> A square root is simplified when:
>
> 1) There are no perfect square factors in any radicand.
> 2) No radicand contains a fraction.
> 3) There are no square roots in any denominator.

Quotient Rule

$$\frac{\sqrt{a}}{\sqrt{b}} = \sqrt{a/b} \quad a \geq 0, b > 0$$

Example 1. Simplify each expression.
   a) $\sqrt{50/2}$ b) $\sqrt{54/2}$ c) $\sqrt{24/3}$

Solution: a) $\sqrt{50/2} = \sqrt{25} = 5$

b) $\sqrt{54/2} = \sqrt{27} = \sqrt{9 \cdot 3} = \sqrt{9} \cdot \sqrt{3} = 3\sqrt{3}$

c) $\sqrt{24/3} = \sqrt{8} = \sqrt{4 \cdot 2} = \sqrt{4} \cdot \sqrt{2} = 2\sqrt{2}$

Example 2. Simplify each expression.
   a) $\frac{\sqrt{x^3}}{\sqrt{x}}$ b) $\frac{\sqrt{12d^5}}{\sqrt{3d}}$ c) $\frac{\sqrt{75x^3y}}{\sqrt{3xy}}$

Solution: a) $\frac{\sqrt{x^3}}{\sqrt{x}} = \sqrt{x^3/x} = \sqrt{x^2} = x$

b) $\frac{\sqrt{12d^5}}{\sqrt{3d}} = \sqrt{12d^5/3d} = \sqrt{4d^4} = 2d^2$

c) $\frac{\sqrt{75x^3y}}{\sqrt{3xy}} = \sqrt{75x^3y^2/3xy} = \sqrt{25x^2y} = 5x\sqrt{y}$

Summary:

> To rationalize a denominator means to remove all radicals from the denominator. To rationalize a denominator, just multiply both the numerator and the denominator of the fraction by the square root that appears in the denominator, or by the square root of a number that makes the denominator a perfect square.

Example 3. Simplify each expression.

   a) $\frac{5}{\sqrt{2}}$ b) $\frac{6}{\sqrt{3}}$ c) $\sqrt{7/2}$ d) $\sqrt{x/6}$

Solution: a) $\dfrac{5}{\sqrt{2}} = \dfrac{5}{\sqrt{2}} \cdot \dfrac{\sqrt{2}}{\sqrt{2}} = \dfrac{5\sqrt{2}}{\sqrt{4}} = \dfrac{5\sqrt{2}}{2}$

b) $\dfrac{6}{\sqrt{3}} = \dfrac{6}{\sqrt{3}} \cdot \dfrac{\sqrt{3}}{\sqrt{3}} = \dfrac{6\sqrt{3}}{\sqrt{9}} = \dfrac{6\sqrt{3}}{3} = 2\sqrt{3}$

c) $\sqrt{7/2} = \dfrac{\sqrt{7}}{\sqrt{2}} = \dfrac{\sqrt{7}}{\sqrt{2}} \cdot \dfrac{\sqrt{2}}{\sqrt{2}} = \dfrac{\sqrt{14}}{2}$

d) $\sqrt{x/6} = \dfrac{\sqrt{x}}{\sqrt{6}} = \dfrac{\sqrt{x}}{\sqrt{6}} \cdot \dfrac{\sqrt{6}}{\sqrt{6}} = \dfrac{\sqrt{6x}}{\sqrt{36}} = \dfrac{\sqrt{6x}}{\sqrt{6}}$

Exercise Set 9.3

Simplify each expression.

1) $\sqrt{36/9}$ 2) $\sqrt{100/5}$ 3) $\dfrac{\sqrt{6}}{\sqrt{54}}$

4) $\dfrac{\sqrt{10}}{\sqrt{1000}}$ 5) $\sqrt{2m^2/18}$ 6) $\sqrt{3/27x^2}$

7) $\sqrt{h^3k^3/16hk^5}$ 8) $\sqrt{m^2/18}$ 9) $\dfrac{\sqrt{45r^3t^7}}{\sqrt{9rt}}$

10) $\sqrt{8m^2n^2/2n^2}$

Simplify each expression.

11) $\dfrac{3}{\sqrt{7}}$ 12) $\dfrac{2}{\sqrt{3}}$ 13) $\dfrac{10}{\sqrt{5}}$

14) $\sqrt{9/7}$ 15) $\sqrt{4/5}$ 16) $\sqrt{2x^2/11x}$

17) $\sqrt{1/x}$ 18) $\dfrac{\sqrt{1}}{\sqrt{a}}$ 19) $\sqrt{28x^2/4y}$

20) $\dfrac{\sqrt{10w^2z}}{\sqrt{30x^2}}$

Answers to Exercise Set 9.3

1) 2 2) $2\sqrt{5}$ 3) $1/3$

4) $1/10$ 5) $m/3$ 6) $1/3x$

7) $h/4k$ 8) $m/3$ 9) $rt^3\sqrt{5}$

10) $2m$ 11) $\dfrac{3\sqrt{7}}{7}$ 12) $\dfrac{2\sqrt{3}}{3}$

13) $2\sqrt{5}$ 14) $\dfrac{3\sqrt{7}}{7}$ 15) $\dfrac{2\sqrt{5}}{5}$

16) $\dfrac{\sqrt{22x}}{11}$ 17) $\dfrac{\sqrt{x}}{x}$ 18) $\dfrac{\sqrt{a}}{a}$

19) $\dfrac{x\sqrt{7y}}{y}$ 20) $\dfrac{w\sqrt{3z}}{3z}$

Roots and Radicals • 175

Section 9.4 Addition and Subtraction of Square Roots

Summary:

> **Like Square Roots**
> To add like square roots, add their coefficients and then multiply that sum by the like square root.
>
> **Unlike Square Roots**
> Unlike square roots cannot be added unless their radicands can be simplified into like square roots.

Example 1.   Simplify each expression, if possible.

a) $5\sqrt{3} + 2\sqrt{3} - 4\sqrt{3}$

b) $7\sqrt{2x} - 3\sqrt{2x}$

c) $\sqrt{32} + \sqrt{72}$

d) $\sqrt{48} + \sqrt{75} - \sqrt{27}$

e) $3\sqrt{17} + 2\sqrt{15}$

Solution:

a) $5\sqrt{3} + 2\sqrt{3} - 4\sqrt{3} = (5+2-4)\sqrt{3} = 3\sqrt{3}$

b) $7\sqrt{2x} - 3\sqrt{2x} = (7-3)\sqrt{2x} = (?)\sqrt{2x}$

c) $\sqrt{32} + \sqrt{72} = \sqrt{16\cdot2} + \sqrt{36\cdot2}$

$= \sqrt{16}\sqrt{2} + \sqrt{36}\sqrt{2}$

$= 4\sqrt{2} + 6\sqrt{2}$

$= (4+6)\sqrt{2}$

$= (?)\sqrt{2}$

d) $\sqrt{48} + \sqrt{75} - \sqrt{27} = \sqrt{16\cdot3} + \sqrt{25\cdot3} - \sqrt{9\cdot3}$

$= \sqrt{16}\sqrt{3} + \sqrt{25}\sqrt{3} - \sqrt{9}\cdot\sqrt{3}$

$= 4\sqrt{3} + 5\sqrt{3} - 3\sqrt{3}$

$= (4+5-3)\sqrt{3} \qquad = (?)\sqrt{3}$

e) $3\sqrt{17} + 2\sqrt{15} = 3\sqrt{17} + 2\sqrt{15}$

Cannot be simplified since the radicands are different.

Answers for (?) in Example 1. b) 4 c) 10 d) 6

Summary:

> Rationalize the denominator of a fractional expression whose denominator is a binomial containing a square root term.
>
> To rationalize the denominator, multiply both the numerator and the denominator of the fraction by the conjugate of the denominator. The conjugate of a binomial is a binomial having the same two terms with the sign of the second term changed.
>
> | Binomial | Conjugate |
> |----------|-----------|
> | $3 + \sqrt{2}$ | $3 - \sqrt{2}$ |
> | $\sqrt{5} - 3$ | $\sqrt{5} + 3$ |
> | $2\sqrt{3} - 5$ | $2\sqrt{3} + 5$ |

Example 2. Multiply $(5 + 3\sqrt{2})(5 - 3\sqrt{2})$

Solution: Use the distributive property.

$$(5 + 3\sqrt{2})(5 - 3\sqrt{2}) = 5(5 - 3\sqrt{2} + 3\sqrt{2}(5 - 3\sqrt{2})$$
$$= (5) \cdot (5) + (5)(-3\sqrt{2}) + 5(3\sqrt{2}) + (3\sqrt{2})(-3\sqrt{2})$$
$$= 25 - 15\sqrt{2} + 15\sqrt{2} - 9\sqrt{4}$$
$$= 25 + 0\sqrt{2} - 9(2)$$
$$= 25 - 18$$
$$= 7$$

Example 3. Multiply $(\sqrt{2} - 7)(\sqrt{2} + 7)$

Solution: Since $(a - b)(a + b) = a^2 - b^2$
where $a = \sqrt{2}$ and $b = 7$ then

$$(\sqrt{2} - 7)(\sqrt{2} + 7) \quad = (\sqrt{2})^2 - (7)^2$$
$$= (?) - 49$$
$$= 2 - 49$$
$$= -(?)$$

Answer for (?) in Example 3.   4 , 47

Example 4.   Simplify $^4/_{(2+\sqrt{5})}$

Solution: $^4/_{(2+\sqrt{5})}$ Conjugate $2 - \sqrt{5}$

$$^4/_{(2+\sqrt{5})} \cdot {}^{(2-\sqrt{5})}/_{(2-\sqrt{5})} = {}^{4(2-\sqrt{5})}/_{(4-5)}$$

$$= {}^{(8-4\sqrt{5})}/_{-1}$$

$$= -8 + 4\sqrt{5}$$

Exercise Set 9.4

Simplify each expression.

1) $5\sqrt{2} + 6\sqrt{2}$ 2) $9\sqrt{5} - 7\sqrt{5}$

3) $3\sqrt{xy} + 7\sqrt{xy}$ 4) $6\sqrt{3w} - \sqrt{3w}$

5) $\sqrt{50} - \sqrt{8}$ 6) $\sqrt{45} + \sqrt{20}$

7) $\sqrt{32} + \sqrt{50}$ 8) $5\sqrt{2y} - \sqrt{8y}$

9) $\sqrt{5x^2} + \sqrt{20x^2}$ 10) $9\sqrt{c^3} - c\sqrt{4c}$

Multiply as indicated.

11) $(4 + \sqrt{2})(4 - \sqrt{2})$ 12) $(8 + \sqrt{5})(8 - \sqrt{5})$

13) $(7 - 2\sqrt{5})(7 + 2\sqrt{5})$ 14) $(3 + \sqrt{x})(3 - \sqrt{x})$

15) $(2\sqrt{y} + 6)(2\sqrt{y} - 6)$ 16) $(3\sqrt{6} - 2\sqrt{3})(3\sqrt{6} + 2\sqrt{3})$

Simplify each expression.

17) $^9/_{(3-\sqrt{12})}$ 18) $^8/_{\sqrt{13}+1}$

19) $^{12}/_{(3-\sqrt{5})}$ 20) $^{3\sqrt{7}+2}/_{2\sqrt{7}-5}$

21) $^3/_{(3+\sqrt{x})}$ 22) $^7/_{3\sqrt{6}-2\sqrt{3}}$

Answers for Exercise Set 9.4

1) $11\sqrt{2}$ 2) $2\sqrt{5}$

3) $10\sqrt{xy}$ 4) $5\sqrt{3w}$

5) $3\sqrt{2}$ 6) $5\sqrt{5}$

7) $9\sqrt{2}$ 8) $3\sqrt{2y}$

9) $3x\sqrt{5}$ 10) $7c\sqrt{c}$

11)   12   12)   59

13)   29   14) $9 - x$

15) $4y - 36$ 16)   42

17) $\dfrac{9(3 + \sqrt{2})}{7}$ 18) $4(\sqrt{3} - 1)$

19) $3(3 + \sqrt{5})$ 20) $\dfrac{(52 + 19\sqrt{7})}{3}$

21) $\dfrac{3(3 - \sqrt{x})}{(9 - x)}$ 22) $\dfrac{(3\sqrt{x} + 2\sqrt{x})}{6}$

Section 9.5 Solving Radical Equations

Summary:

> A radical equation is an equation that contains a variable in a radicand.
>
> **To Solve a Radical Equation Containing Only One Square Root Term.**
>
> 1) Use the appropriate properties to rewrite the equation with the square root term by itself on one side of the equation.
> 2) Combine like terms.
> 3) Square both sides of the equation to remove the square root.
> 4) Solve the equation for the variable.
> 5) Check the solution in the original equation for extraneous roots.

Example 1.   Solve the equation $\sqrt{x} = 7$

Solution: Since Step 1 and Step 2 do not apply, start at Step 3.

$$\sqrt{x} = 7$$
$$(\text{Step 3}) \ (\sqrt{x})^2 = (7)^2$$
$$\sqrt{x}^{\,2} = 49$$

$$(\text{Step 4}) \qquad x = 49$$

$$(\text{Step 5}) \quad \sqrt{x} = 7 \qquad \text{Check:}$$
$$\sqrt{49} = 7$$

$$7 = 7 \quad \textit{True} \qquad \text{The solution is 49.}$$

Example 2.   Solve the equation $\sqrt{x-5} = 3$

Solution: Since Step 1 and Step 2 do not apply, start at Step 3.
$$\sqrt{x-5} = 3$$

(Step 3) $(\sqrt{x-5})^2 = (3)^2$
(Step 4) $x - 5 = 9$
$x = 14$
(Step 5) $\sqrt{x-5} = 3$ Check:
$\sqrt{(?)-5} = 3$
$\sqrt{9} = 3$
$3 = 3$ *True*

The solution is 14.

Answer for (?) in Example 2. 14

Example 3.   Solve the equation $\sqrt{5x} = -5$

Solution: Since Step 1 and Step 2 do not apply, start at Step 3.
$$\sqrt{5x} = -5$$

(Step 3) $(\sqrt{5x})^2 = (-5)^2$
(Step 4) $5x = 25$
$x = 5$
(Step 5) $\sqrt{5x} = -5$ Check:
$\sqrt{5(?)} = -5$
$\sqrt{5 \cdot 5} = -5$
$\sqrt{25} = -5$
$5 = -5$ **False**

5 is not a solution to the equation.

Example 4.   Solve the equation $2z + \sqrt{2z} = 2$

Solution: $2z + \sqrt{2z} = 2$
(Step 1) $\sqrt{2z} = 2 - 2z$
(Step 2)   Does not apply.
$\sqrt{2z} = 2 - 2z$

(Step 3) $\sqrt{2z}^2 = (2-2z)^2$
$\sqrt{2z}^2 = (2-2z)(2-2z)$
$4z^2 = 4 - 4z - 4z + 4z^2$
$2z = 4 - 8z + 4z^2$

(Step 4) $0 = 4z^2 - 8z - 2z + 4$

$0 = 4z^2 - 10z + 4$

$0 = 2(2z^2 - 5z + 2)$

$0 = 2(2z - 1)(z - 2)$

$2z - 1 = 0$ or $z - 2 = 0$

$2z = 1$ $z = 2$

$z = {}^1/_2$

(Step) Check: $z = {}^1/_2$ $z = 2$

$2(?) + \sqrt{2(?)} = 2$ $2(?) + \sqrt{2(?)} = 2$

$2\,{}^1/_2 + \sqrt{2\,{}^1/_2} = 2$ $2(2) + \sqrt{2(2)} = 2$

$1 + \sqrt{1} = 2$ $4 + \sqrt{4} = 2$

$1 + 1 = 2$ $4 + 2 = 2$

$2 = 2$ *True* $6 = 2$ *False*

The solution is ${}^1/_2$; 2 is not a solution.

Answers for (?) in Example 4. ${}^1/_2, {}^1/_2, 2, 2$

Example 5.   Solve the equation $\sqrt{5x + 6} = \sqrt{9x - 2}$

Solution: Start at Step 3.

(Step 3) $\sqrt{5x + 6} = \sqrt{9x - 2}$

$(\sqrt{5x + 6})^2 = (\sqrt{9x - 2})^2$

(Step 4) $5x + 6 = 9x - 2$

$6 = 9x - 5x - 2$

$6 = 4x - 2$

$6 + 2 = 4x$

$8 = 4x$

$2 = x$

(Step 5) $\sqrt{5x + 6} = \sqrt{9x - 2}$ Check:

$\sqrt{5(?) + 6} = \sqrt{9(?) - 2}$

$\sqrt{5(2) + 6} = \sqrt{9(2) - 2}$

$\sqrt{10 + 6} = \sqrt{18 - 2}$

$\sqrt{16} = \sqrt{16}$

$4 = 4$ *True*

The solution is 2.

Exercise Set 9.5

Solve each equation.

1) $\sqrt{y} = 4$ 2) $\sqrt{y} = -4$

3) $\sqrt{3x} = 2$ 4) $4\sqrt{x} = 8$

5) $2\sqrt{3x} = 6$ 6) $\sqrt{x+3} = 5$

7) $\sqrt{2b-1} = 3$ 8) $\sqrt{2b+2} = 6$

9) $\sqrt{5a-1} - 3 = 0$ 10) $4\sqrt{a+7} - 5 = 11$

11) $2 - \sqrt{2z} = 2$ 12) $\sqrt{2x^2+4} = x+2$

13) $\sqrt{x^2+3} = x+1$ 14) $x = 4 + \sqrt{x^2+32}$

15) $\sqrt{9-2x} = \sqrt{5x-12}$ 16) $5\sqrt{2x+8} = 3\sqrt{26-2x}$

17) $\sqrt{x+1} = \sqrt{2x-7}$ 18) $\sqrt{3x-2} = \sqrt{x+4}$

Answers for Exercise Set 9.5

1)	16	2)	No solution	3)	$^4/_3$
4)	4	5)	3	6)	22
7)	8	8)	8	9)	2
10)	9	11)	0	12)	0, 4
13)	1	14)	6	15)	3
16)	$^1/_2$	17)	8	18)	3

Section 9.6 Applications of Radicals

Summary:

A right triangle is a triangle that contains a right or 90 degree angle.

The two smaller sides of a right triangle are called the legs and the side opposite the right angle is called the hypotenuse.

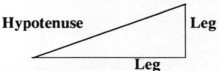

Pythagorean Theorem

The square of the hypotenuse of a right triangle is equal to the sum of the squares of the two legs.

If **a** and **b** represent the legs, and c represent the hypotenuse, then
$$a^2 + b^2 = c^2$$

Example 1.   Find the hypotenuse of the right triangle whose legs are 5 feet and 12 feet.

Solution:

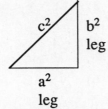

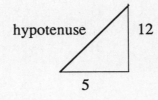

It makes no difference which leg is a and which leg is b.

$$c^2 = a^2 + b^2$$
$$c^2 = (5)^2 + (12)^2$$
$$c^2 = 25 + 144, \quad c^2 = 169$$
$$\sqrt{c^2} = \sqrt{169}$$
$$c = 13$$

The hypotenuse is 13.

Check:
$$a^2 + b^2 = c^2$$
$$5^2 + (12)^2 = (13)^2$$
$$25 + 144 = 169$$
$$169 = 169 \qquad \textbf{\textit{True}}$$

Example 2.   The hypotenuse of a right triangle is 25 inches. Find the second leg if one leg is 24 inches.

Solution:
$$c^2 = a^2 + b^2$$
$$(25)^2 = (24)^2 + b^2$$
$$625 = 576 + b^2$$
$$625 - 576 = b^2$$
$$49 = b^2$$
$$7 = b$$

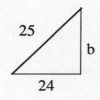

The other leg is 7 inches.

Summary:

Distance Formula
$$d = \sqrt{(x_2 - x_1)^2 + (y_2 - y_1)^2}$$

Example 3.   Find the length of the straight line between the points (2, 3) and (5, 7).

Solution: It makes no difference which points are labeled (x_1, y_1) and (x_2, y_2).

Let (2, 3) be (x_1, y_1) and (5, 7) be (x_2, y_2)
Thus $x_1 = 2$ $y_1 = 3$ and $x_2 = 5$ $y_2 = 7$

$$d = \sqrt{(x_2 - x_1)^2 + (y_2 - y_1)^2}$$
$$d = \sqrt{(5 - 2)^2 + (7 - 3)^2}$$
$$d = \sqrt{(3)^2 + (4)^2}$$
$$d = \sqrt{9 + 16}$$
$$d = \sqrt{25}$$
$$d = 5$$

The distance between (2, 3) and (5, 7) is 5 units.

Example 3.   Find the side of a square that has an area of 324 square inches.
Use $A = s^2$

Solution:
$$A = s^2$$
$$324 = s^2$$
$$\sqrt{324} = \sqrt{s^2}$$
$$18 = s$$

Thus each side is 18 inches.

Exercise Set 9.6

Use the pythagorean theorem to find the quantity indicated. You may leave your answer in square root form if a calculator with a square root key is not available and the number is not a perfect square.

1) Find the hypotenuse of a right triangle whose legs are 12 and 16.

2) Find the hypotenuse of a right triangle whose legs are 6 and 2.

3) Find the hypotenuse of a right triangle whose legs are $\sqrt{17}$ and $\sqrt{19}$.

4) The hypotenuse of a right triangle is 6 units. Find the second leg if one leg is 4 units.

5) The hypotenuse of a right triangle is $3\sqrt{3}$ units. Find the second leg is one leg is 3 units.

6) The hypotenuse of a right triangle is $2\sqrt{6}$ units. Find the second leg if one leg is 4 units.

7) A 25 foot extension ladder is placed against a house. The base of the ladder is 7 feet from the house. How high is the top of the ladder?

8) Find the length of the diagonals of a 7 inch by 12 inch rectangle.

9) Find the length of the diagonals of a square with side equal to 5 feet.

10) Keith Murphy leans a 30 foot ladder against a building. If the base of the ladder is 4 feet from the building, how far up the building does the ladder reach?

11) Find the length of the straight line between the points (4, 2) and (-2, 4).

12) Find the length of the straight line between the points (3, 5) and (6, 9).

13) Find the length of the straight line between the points (0, 2) and (12, 7).

14) Find the length of the straight line between the points (6, -9) and (-6, 9).

15) Find the side of a square that has an area of 10,000 square units. Use $A = s^2$

16) Find the side of a square that has an area of 400 square units. Use $A = s^2$

17) Find the side of a square that has an area of 45 square units. Use $A = s^2$

18) A formula for the area of a circle is $A = \pi r^2$, where π is approximately 3.14 and r is the radius of the circle. Find the radius of a circle of area 78.5 square inches.

19) Find the radius of a circle with an area of 706.5 square feet.

20) Find the radius of a circle with an area of 153.86 square inches.

Answers to Exercise Set 9.6

1)	20	2)	$2\sqrt{10}$ or 6.32
3)	6	4)	$2\sqrt{5}$ or 4.47
5)	$3\sqrt{2}$ or 4.24	6)	$2\sqrt{2}$ or 2.83
7)	24 feet	8)	$\sqrt{193}$ or 13.89
9)	$5\sqrt{2}$ or 7.07	10)	$\sqrt{884}$ or 29.73 feet
11)	$2\sqrt{10}$ or 6.32	12)	5
13)	13	14)	$\sqrt{468}$ or 21.63
15)	100	16)	20
17)	$3\sqrt{5}$ or 6.71	18)	5
19)	15	20)	7

Summary:

$^3\sqrt{a}$ is read "the cube root of **a**"

$^4\sqrt{a}$ is read "the fourth root of **a**"

$^3\sqrt{a} = b$ if $b^3 = \mathbf{a}$

$^4\sqrt{a} = b$ if $b^4 = \mathbf{a}$

Example 1. Evaluate

a) $^3\sqrt{8}$ b) $^3\sqrt{64}$ c) $^3\sqrt{-8}$ d) $^3\sqrt{-64}$

Solution:

a) $^3\sqrt{8} = 2$ since $2^3 = 2 \cdot 2 \cdot 2 = 8$

b) $^3\sqrt{64} = 4$ since $4^3 = 4 \cdot 4 \cdot 4 = 64$

c) $^3\sqrt{-8} = -2$ since $(-2)^3 = (-2)(-2)(-2) = -8$

d) $^3\sqrt{-64} = -4$ since $(-4)^3 = (-4)(-4)(-4) = -64$

Example 2. Evaluate

a) $^4\sqrt{81}$ b) $^4\sqrt{256}$ c) $^4\sqrt{10,000}$

Solution:

a) $^4\sqrt{81} = 3$ since $3^4 = 3 \cdot 3 \cdot 3 \cdot 3 = 81$

b) $^4\sqrt{256} = 4$ since $4^4 = 4 \cdot 4 \cdot 4 \cdot 4 = 256$

c) $^4\sqrt{10,000} = 10$ since $10^4 = 10 \cdot 10 \cdot 10 \cdot 10 = 10,000$

➥**Note:** The cube root of a positive number is a positive number and the cube root of a negative number is a negative number.

The radicand of a fourth root (or any even root) must be a nonnegative number for the expression to be a real number.

Summary:

Product Rule for Radicals.

$$^n\sqrt{a} \ \ ^n\sqrt{b} = \ ^n\sqrt{ab} \text{ for } \mathbf{a} \geq 0, \mathbf{b} \geq 0$$

Rename a radical in exponential form.

$$^n\sqrt{a} = a^{1/n} \quad a > 0$$

$$^n\sqrt{a^m} = a^{n/m} \quad \text{for } \mathbf{a} > 0 \text{ and m and n integers.}$$

Example 3. Simplify

a) $\sqrt[3]{24}$ 　　b) $\sqrt[3]{88}$ 　　c) $\sqrt[4]{32}$ 　　d) $\sqrt[4]{162}$

Solution:　　a) $\sqrt[3]{24} = \sqrt[3]{8 \cdot 3} = \sqrt[3]{8} \cdot \sqrt[3]{3} = 2\sqrt[3]{3}$

b) $\sqrt[3]{88} = \sqrt[3]{8 \cdot 11} = \sqrt[3]{8} \cdot \sqrt[3]{11} = 2\sqrt[3]{11}$

c) $\sqrt[4]{32} = \sqrt[4]{16 \cdot 2} = \sqrt[4]{16} \cdot \sqrt[4]{2} = 2\sqrt[4]{2}$

d) $\sqrt[4]{162} = \sqrt[4]{81 \cdot 2} = \sqrt[4]{81} \cdot \sqrt[4]{2} = 3\sqrt[4]{2}$

Example 4. Simplify

a) $\sqrt[3]{x^5} = \sqrt[3]{x^3 \cdot x^2} = \sqrt[3]{x^3} \cdot \sqrt[3]{x^2} = x\sqrt[3]{x^2}$

b) $\sqrt[3]{x^6 y^{10}} = \sqrt[3]{x^6 y^9 \cdot y} = \sqrt[3]{x^6 y^9} \cdot \sqrt[3]{y} = x^2 y^3 \sqrt[3]{y}$

c) $\sqrt[4]{x^5} = \sqrt[4]{x^4 \cdot x} = \sqrt[4]{x^4} \cdot \sqrt[4]{x} = x\sqrt[4]{x}$

d) $\sqrt[4]{x^6 y^{10}} = \sqrt[4]{x^4 x^2 y^8 y^2} = \sqrt[4]{x^4 y^8} \cdot \sqrt[4]{x^2 y^2} = xy^2 \sqrt[4]{x^2 y^2}$

Example 5. Evaluate

a) $16^{3/2}$ 　　b) $(-8)^{2/3}$ 　　c) $64^{1/4}$ 　　d) $49^{1/2}$

Solution:　　a) $16^{3/2} = (\sqrt[2]{16})^3 = (4)^3 = 64$

b) $(-8)^{2/3} = (\sqrt[3]{-8})^2 = (-2)^2 = 4$

c) $64^{1/4} = (\sqrt[4]{64})^1 = (4)^1 = 4$

d) $49^{1/2} = (\sqrt[2]{49})^1 = (7)^1 = 7$

Example 6. Write each of the following in exponential form.

a) $\sqrt[4]{y^6}$ 　　b) $\sqrt{x^3 y^7}$ 　　c) $\sqrt[3]{x^7}$ 　　d) $\sqrt[3]{19 y^5}$

Solution:

a) $\sqrt[4]{y^6} = y^{6/4} = y^{3/2}$

b) $\sqrt{x^3 y^7} = (x^3 y^7)^{1/2} = x^{3/2} y^{7/2}$

c) $\sqrt[3]{x^7} = x^{7/3}$

d) $\sqrt[4]{19 y^5} = (19 y^5)^{1/3} = 19^{1/3} y^{5/3}$

Example 7.   Simpl ify

$$a)\ \sqrt{y^3}\ \sqrt[4]{y} \qquad b)\ (\sqrt[4]{w^3})^8$$

Solution: a) $\sqrt{y^3}\ \sqrt[4]{y}\ = y^{3/2} \cdot y^{1/4}$

$$= y^{3/2\ +\ 1/4}$$

$$= y^{6/4\ +\ 1/4}$$

$$= y^{7/4}$$

$$= \sqrt[4]{y^7}$$

b) $(\sqrt[4]{w^3})^8\ = (w^{3/4})^8$

$$= w^{24/4}$$

$$= w^6$$

Exercise Set 9.7

Evaluate each of the following.

1) $\sqrt[3]{64}$ 2) $\sqrt[4]{81}$ 3) $\sqrt[3]{-1}$

4) $\sqrt[3]{-125}$ 5) $\sqrt[4]{1}$ 6) $\sqrt[3]{-343}$

7) $\sqrt[4]{1296}$ 8) $\sqrt[3]{-1000}$ 9) $\sqrt[4]{625}$

Simplify each of the following.

10) $\sqrt[3]{48}$ 11) $\sqrt[4]{243}$ 12) $\sqrt[3]{54}$

13) $\sqrt[4]{128}$ 14) $\sqrt[3]{192}$ 15) $\sqrt[4]{80}$

Simplify each of the following.

16) $\sqrt[3]{x^7}$ 17) $\sqrt[4]{x^5}$ 18) $\sqrt[3]{x^{30}}$

19) $\sqrt[4]{x^{25}}$ 20) $\sqrt[3]{y^{17}}$ 24) $\sqrt[4]{x^{14}}$

Evaluate each of the following.

22) $(-125)^{1/3}$ 23) $(81)^{3/4}$ 24) $(-1000)^{2/3}$

Write each radical in exponential form.

25) $\sqrt[3]{x^5}$ 26) $\sqrt[4]{y^7}$ 27) $\sqrt[4]{x^{13}}$

Simplify each of the following.

28) $\sqrt[3]{y^2} \cdot \sqrt[4]{y}$ 29) $\sqrt[3]{y}\ \sqrt[3]{y^2}$ 30) $(\sqrt[4]{x^7})^{16}$

Answers for Exercise Set 9.7

1)	4	2)	3	3)	-1
4)	-5	5)	1	6)	-7
7)	6	8)	-10	9)	5
10)	$2^3\sqrt{6}$	11)	$3^4\sqrt{3}$	12)	$3^3\sqrt{2}$
13)	$2^4\sqrt{8}$	14)	$4^3\sqrt{3}$	15)	$2^4\sqrt{5}$
16)	$x^2(^3\sqrt{x})$	17)	$x(^4\sqrt{x})$	18)	x^{10}
19)	$x^6(^4\sqrt{x})$	20)	$y^5(^3\sqrt{y^2})$	21)	$y^3(^4\sqrt{y^2})$
22)	-5	23)	27	24)	100
25)	$x^{5/3}$	26)	$y^{7/4}$	27)	$x^{13/2}$
28)	$y^{11/12}$	29)	y	30)	x^{28}

Practice Test Chapter 9

Simplify each expression.

1) $\sqrt{27}$ 2) $\sqrt{300}$ 3) $\sqrt{18}$ 4) $\sqrt{8}$

5) $\sqrt{63x^2}$ 6) $\sqrt{12x^3y^2}$ 7) $\sqrt{80x^4y^3}$ 8) $\sqrt{32^2}$

9) $\sqrt{2/5}$ 10) $\sqrt{7/36}$ 11) $\sqrt{5/3}$ 12) $\sqrt{7/x}$

13) $\sqrt{11/48x^2}$ 14) $\sqrt{5x^3/4x}$ 15) $\sqrt{27x^2y/3x^2y^3}$ 16) $\sqrt{3} \cdot \sqrt{18}$

17) $\sqrt{7x} \cdot \sqrt{21x}$ 18) $7\sqrt{6} - 3\sqrt{6}$ 19) $\sqrt{98} - \sqrt{128} + \sqrt{32}$

20) $3\sqrt{y} + 7\sqrt{y} - 2\sqrt{y}$ 21) $2/(1+\sqrt{7})$ 22) $5/(3-\sqrt{5})$

Solve each equation.

23) $\sqrt{7y+2} - 4 = 0$ 24) $\sqrt{2x^2-1} + 3 = 2x$

25) Find the hypotenuse of a right triangle given the legs are $\sqrt{5}$ and 2.

26) Find the length of a straight line between the points (-7, 5) and (4, 5).

27) Evaluate $64^{2/3}$ 28) $^3\sqrt{24x^6y^4}$

Answers for Practice Test Chapter 9

1) $3\sqrt{3}$ 2) $10\sqrt{3}$ 3) $3\sqrt{2}$

4) $2\sqrt{2}$ 5) $3x\sqrt{7}$ 6) $2xy\sqrt{3x}$

7) $4x^2y\sqrt{5y}$ 8) 32 9) $\frac{\sqrt{10}}{5}$

10) $\frac{\sqrt{7}}{6}$ 11) $\frac{\sqrt{15}}{3}$ 12) $\frac{\sqrt{7x}}{x}$

13) $\frac{\sqrt{33}}{12x}$ 14) $\frac{x\sqrt{5}}{2}$ 15) $^3/_y$

16) $3\sqrt{6}$ 17) $7x\sqrt{3}$ 18) $4\sqrt{6}$

19) $3\sqrt{2}$ 20) $8\sqrt{y}$ 21) $\frac{(1-\sqrt{7})}{-3}$

22) $\frac{5(3+\sqrt{5})}{4}$ 23) 2 24) 5

25) 3 26) 11 27) 16

28) $2x^3y(^3\sqrt{3})$

❖❖❖❖❖❖❖❖❖❖❖❖❖❖

Chapter 10 Quadratic Equations

Section 10.1 The Square Root Property

Summary:

> **Quadratic Equation in standard form:**
>
> $$ax^2 + bx + c = 0 \qquad \text{a, b, c are real numbers. a} \neq 0.$$
>
> **Square Root Property:**
>
> If $\quad x^2 = a$
> then $\quad \sqrt{x^2} = \pm \sqrt{a}$
>
> and $\quad x = \pm a$

Example 1. Solve the equation $x^2 - 64 = 0$

Solution: In order to apply the square root property, get the variable all by itself on one side of the equation.

$$
\begin{aligned}
x^2 &= 64 \\
x^2 - 64 + 64 &= 0 + 64 \\
x^2 &= 64 \\
\sqrt{x^2} &= \sqrt{64} \\
x &= \pm 8
\end{aligned}
$$

Meaning $x = 8$ or $x = -8$

Check:

$x = 8$	$x = -8$
$x^2 - 64 = 0$	$x^2 - 64 = 0$
$(8)^2 - 64 = 0$	$(-8)^2 - 64 = 0$
$64 - 64 = 0$	$64 - 64 = 0$
$0 = 0$ *True*	$0 = 0$ *True*

Example 2. Solve the equation $3x^2 = 21$

Solution:
$$
\begin{aligned}
3x^2 &= 21 \\
x^2 &= 7 \\
\sqrt{x^2} &= \pm \sqrt{7} \\
x &= \sqrt{7} \text{ or } x = -\sqrt{7}
\end{aligned}
$$

Example 3. Solve the equation $(x - 5)^2 = 7$

Solution

$$(x - 5)^2 = 7$$
$$\sqrt{(x - 5)^2} = \sqrt{7}$$
$$x - 5 = \pm \sqrt{7}$$
$$x - 5 = \sqrt{7} \quad \text{or} \quad x - 5 = -\sqrt{7}$$
$$x = 5 + \sqrt{7} \qquad\qquad x = 5 - \sqrt{7}$$

Example 4. Bill Lee wants to buy wall to wall carpet for a room in his house. The length of his room is twice the width. Find the dimensions of the rectangular room if he needs 200 square feet of carpet.

Solution: Let x = width; then $2x$ = length
area = length • width

$$200 = 2x \cdot x$$
$$200 = 2x^2$$
$$100 = x^2$$
$$\sqrt{100} = \sqrt{x^2}$$
$$\pm 10 = x$$
$$x = 10 \qquad \text{or} \qquad x = -10$$

Since distance cannot be negative, the width, x, is 10 and the length is 2(10) or 20.

Exercise Set 10.1

Solve each equation.

1) $x^2 = 25$

2) $x^2 = 81$

3) $x^2 - 225 = 0$

4) $25x^2 - 4 = 0$

5) $4x^2 = 24$

6) $5y^2 = 65$

7) $7a^2 - 56 = 0$

8) $6y^2 - 24 = 0$

9) $4x^2 + 3x^2 = 35$

10) $7x^2 = 4x^2 + 72$

11) $(x + 2)^2 = 25$

12) $(y - 15)^2 = 36$

13) $8 = (x - 8)^2$

14) $12 = (x + 12)^2$

15) $(3x + 7)^2 = 64$

16) $(2x + 5)^2 = 3$

17) Linda Chapman wants to repaper a hallway wall. The length is 3 times the width. Find the dimensions if she purchased 243 square feet of paper.

18) Chuck Gurtler wants to purchase grub treatment chemicals for his lawn. The length of his lawn is twice the width. Find the dimensions of his lawn if he purchased chemical to treat 20,000 square feet of lawn.

Answers to Exercise Set 10.1

1) ± 5	2) ± 9	3) ± 15	4) $\pm \frac{2}{5}$

5) $\pm \sqrt{6}$ or ± 2.449 6) $\pm \sqrt{13}$ or ± 3.606

7) $\pm \sqrt{8}$ or ± 2.828 8) ± 2

9) $\pm \sqrt{5}$ or ± 2.236 10) $\pm 2\sqrt{6}$ or ± 4.899

11) $3, -7$ 12) $9, 21$

13) $8 + 2\sqrt{2}, 8 - 2\sqrt{2}$ 14) $-12 + 2\sqrt{3}, 12 - 2\sqrt{3}$

15) $\frac{1}{3}, -5$ 16) $\frac{-5 + \sqrt{3}}{2}, \frac{-5 - \sqrt{3}}{2}$

17)   9 ft. width   18)   100 ft. width
        27 ft. length   200 ft. length

Section 10.2 Solving Quadratic Equations by Completing the Square.

Summary:

> **To Solve a Quadratic Equation by Completing the Square:**
>
> 1) Use the multiplication (or division) property if necessary to make the numerical coefficient of the squared term equal to 1.
>
> 2) Rewrite the equation with the constant by itself on the right side of the equation.
>
> 3) Take one-half the numerical coefficient of the first-powered term, square it, and add this quantity to both sides of the equation.
>
> 4) Replace the trinomial with its equivalent squared binomial.
>
> 5) Take the square root of both sides of the equation.
>
> 6) Solve for the variable.
>
> 7) Check your answers in the original equation.

Example 1.   Solve the equation $x^2 - 2x - 8 = 0$ by completing the square.

Solution: Since Step 1 does not apply, start at Step 2.

$$x^2 - 2x - 8 = 0$$

(Step 2) $$x^2 - 2x = 8$$

(Step 3) $$\tfrac{1}{2}(-2) = -1 \qquad = \qquad (-1)^2 = 1$$
$$x^2 - 2x + 1 = 8 + 1$$

(Step 4) $$(x - 1)^2 = 9$$

(Step 5) $$\sqrt{(x - 1)^2} = \sqrt{9}$$
$$x - 1 = \pm 3$$

(Step 6) $$x - 1 = 3 \qquad \text{or} \qquad x - 1 = -3$$
$$x = 4 \qquad\qquad\qquad\qquad x = -2$$

(Step 7)   Check: $x = 4$ $\qquad\qquad\qquad\qquad$ $x = -2$

$$x^2 - 2x - 8 = 0 \qquad\qquad x^2 - 2x - 8 = 0$$
$$(4)^2 - 2(4) - 8 = 0 \qquad (-2)^2 - 2(-2) - 8 = 0$$
$$16 - 8 - 8 = 0 \qquad\qquad 4 + 4 - 8 = 0$$
$$16 - 16 = 0 \qquad\qquad\qquad 8 - 8 = 0$$
$$0 = 0 \quad \textbf{\textit{True}} \qquad\qquad 0 = 0 \quad \textbf{\textit{True}}$$

The solutions are 4 and -2.

Example 2.   Solve the equation $x^2 - x - 6 = 0$ by completing the square.

Solution: Since Step 1 does not apply, start at Step 2.

(Step 2) $$x^2 - x - 6 = 0$$
$$x^2 - x = 6$$

(Step 3) $$\tfrac{1}{2}(-1) = -\tfrac{1}{2} = (-\tfrac{1}{2})^2 = \tfrac{1}{4}$$
$$x^2 - x + \tfrac{1}{4} = 6 + \tfrac{1}{4}$$
$$x^2 - x + \tfrac{1}{4} = \tfrac{24}{4} + \tfrac{1}{4}$$
$$x^2 - x + \tfrac{1}{4} = \tfrac{25}{4}$$

(Step 4) $$(x - \tfrac{1}{2})^2 = \tfrac{25}{4}$$

(Step 5) $$\sqrt{(x - \tfrac{1}{2})^2} = \sqrt{\tfrac{25}{4}}$$

(Step 6) $$x - \tfrac{1}{2} = \pm \tfrac{5}{2}$$
$$x - \tfrac{1}{2} = \tfrac{5}{2} \qquad \text{or} \qquad x - \tfrac{1}{2} = -\tfrac{5}{2}$$
$$x = \tfrac{6}{2} \qquad\qquad\qquad\qquad x = -\tfrac{4}{2}$$
$$x = 3 \qquad\qquad\qquad\qquad\quad x = -2$$

The solutions are 3 and -2.

Example 3.   Solve the equation $2x^2 + 5x = 12$

Solution:

$$2x^2 + 5x = 12$$

(Step 1) $$\tfrac{1}{2}(2x^2 + 5x) = \tfrac{1}{2}(12)$$

$$\tfrac{2x^2}{2} + \tfrac{5}{2}x = \tfrac{12}{2}$$

$$x^2 + \tfrac{5}{2}x = 6$$

(Step 3) $$\tfrac{1}{2} \cdot \tfrac{5}{2} = \tfrac{5}{4} = \quad (\tfrac{5}{4})^2 = \tfrac{25}{16}$$

$$x^2 + \tfrac{5}{2}x + \tfrac{25}{16} = 6 + \tfrac{25}{16}$$

$$x^2 + \tfrac{5}{2}x + \tfrac{25}{16} = \tfrac{96}{16} + \tfrac{25}{16}$$

$$x^2 + \tfrac{5}{2}x + \tfrac{25}{16} = \tfrac{121}{16}$$

(Step 4) $$(x + \tfrac{5}{2})^2 = \tfrac{121}{16}$$

(Step 5) $$\sqrt{(x + \tfrac{5}{2})^2} = \sqrt{\tfrac{121}{16}}$$

$$x + \tfrac{5}{2} = \pm \tfrac{11}{4}$$

(Step 6) $$x + \tfrac{5}{2} = \tfrac{11}{4} \qquad \text{or} \qquad x - \tfrac{5}{2} = -\tfrac{11}{4}$$

$$x = \tfrac{11}{4} - \tfrac{5}{2} \qquad\qquad x = -\tfrac{11}{4} + \tfrac{5}{2}$$

$$x = \tfrac{11}{4} - \tfrac{10}{4} \qquad\qquad x = -\tfrac{11}{4} + \tfrac{10}{4}$$

$$x = \tfrac{1}{4} \qquad\qquad\qquad x = -\tfrac{1}{4}$$

The solutions are $\tfrac{1}{4}$ and $-\tfrac{1}{4}$.

Exercise Set 10.2

Solve each equation by completing the square.

1) $x^2 - 4x - 12 = 0$ 2) $x^2 + 4x - 21 = 0$

3) $x^2 + x - 12 = 0$ 4) $x^2 - 2x - 15 = 0$

5) $x^2 - 8x + 4 = 0$ 6) $2x^2 + 5x = 12$

7) $6x^2 = 11x + 10$ 8) $8x^2 - 6x + 1 = 0$

9) $4x^2 - 4x + 1 = 0$ 10) $3x^2 - 2x - 3 = 0$

Answers to Exercise Set 10.2

1) -2, 6   2) -7, 3

3) -4, 3   4) -3, 5

5) $4 + 2\sqrt{3}$, $4 - 2\sqrt{3}$ 6) -4, $\tfrac{3}{2}$

7) $-\tfrac{2}{3}$, $\tfrac{5}{2}$ 8) $\tfrac{1}{4}$, $\tfrac{1}{2}$

9) $\tfrac{1}{2}$, $\tfrac{1}{2}$ 10) $\tfrac{(1 + \sqrt{10})}{3}$, $\tfrac{(1 \sqrt{10})}{3}$

Section 10.3   Solving Quadratic Equations by the Quadratic Formula

Summary:

> **To Solve a Quadratic Equation by the Quadratic Formula**
>
> 1) Write the equation in standard form, $ax^2 + bx + c = 0$, and determine the numerical values for **a, b,** and **c.**
>
> 2) Substitute the values for **a, b,** and **c** in the quadratic formula and then evaluate to obtain the solution.
>
> **The quadratic formula**
>
> $$x = \frac{-b \pm \sqrt{b^2 - 4ac}}{2a}$$

Example 1.   Solve the equation $x^2 - 2x - 8 = 0$ using the quadratic formula.

Solution: $ax^2 + bx + c = 0$

(Step 1) $1x^2 - 2x - 8 = 0$
               $a = 1 \qquad b = -2 \qquad c = -8$

(Step 2) $x = \frac{-b \pm \sqrt{b^2 - 4ac}}{2a}$

$$x = \frac{-(-2) \pm \sqrt{(-2)^2 - 4(1)(-8)}}{2(1)}$$

$$x = \frac{2 \pm \sqrt{4 + 32}}{2}$$

$$x = \frac{2 \pm \sqrt{36}}{2}$$

$$x = \frac{2 \pm 6}{2}$$

$$x = \frac{2 + 6}{2} \quad \text{or} \quad x = \frac{2 - 6}{2}$$

$$x = \frac{8}{2} \qquad\qquad x = \frac{-4}{2}$$

$$x = 4 \qquad\qquad x = -2$$

The solutions are 4 and -2.

Example 2.   Solve the equation $x^2 - 8x = -4$

Solution: $x^2 - 8x = -4$
(Step 1) $ax^2 + bx + c = 0$
              $1x^2 - 8x + 4 = 0$
                        $a = 1$ $b = -8$ $c = 4$

(Step 2) $x = \left[-b \pm \sqrt{b^2 - 4ac} \right]/2a$

              $x = \left[-(-8) \pm \sqrt{(-8)^2 - 4(1)(4)} \right]/2(1)$

              $x = \left[8 \pm \sqrt{64 - 16} \right]/2$

              $x = \left(8 \pm \sqrt{48} \right)/2$

              $x = \left(8 \pm \sqrt{16 \cdot 3} \right)/2$, $x = \left(8 \pm 4\sqrt{3} \right)/2$

              $x = \left(8 + 4\sqrt{3} \right)/2$ or $x = \left(8 - 4\sqrt{3} \right)/2$

              $x = 4 + 2\sqrt{3}$ $x = 4 - 2\sqrt{3}$

The solutions are $4 + 2\sqrt{3}$ and $4 - 2\sqrt{3}$.

Example 3.   Solve the equation $3x^2 = 2x - 3$

Solution: $3x^2 = 2x - 3$

(Step 1) $ax^2 + bx + c = 0$
              $3x^2 - 2x + 3 = 0$
                        $a = 3$ $b = -2$ $c = 3$

(Step 2) $x = \left[-b \pm \sqrt{b^2 - 4ac} \right]/2a$

              $x = \left[-(-2 \pm \sqrt{(-2)^2 - 4(3)(3)} \right]/2(3)$

              $x = 2 \pm \sqrt{4 - 36}/6$

              $x = 2 \pm \sqrt{-32}/6$

Since $\sqrt{-32}$ is not a real number, you can go no further. This question will be solved later in intermediate algebra. When given a problem of this type, your **answer should be no real solution.** Do not leave the answer blank, and do not write 0 for the answer.

Summary:

> The discriminant is used to determine the number of solutions to a quadratic equation.
>
> $$b^2 - 4ac$$
> discriminant
>
> When the discriminant is:
>
> 1) **Greater than zero,** $b^2 - 4ac > 0$,   (positive number) the quadratic equation has two distinct solutions.
>
> 2) **Equal to zero,** $b^2 - 4ac = 0$, the quadratic equation has a single unique solution. This single solution is often referred to as a double root.
>
> 3) **Less than zero,** $b^2 - 4ac < 0$,   (negative number) the quadratic equation has no real solution.

Example 4.   Find the discriminant of the equation
$3x^2 - 2x + 3 = 0$

Solution: $a = 3$ $b = -2$ $c = 3$

$$\begin{aligned} b^2 - 4ac &= (-2)^2 - 4\,(3)(3) \\ &= 4 - 36 \\ &= -32 \end{aligned}$$

Since the discriminant is less than zero, the quadratic equation, if solved, would have no real solution.

Example 5.   Without actually finding the solutions, determine if the following equations have two distinct solution, a single unique solution, or no real solutions.

a) $4x^2 - 4x + 1 = 0$

b) $6x^2 - 11x + 10 = 0$

c) $8x^2 - 6x + 1 = 0$

Solution: a) $4x^2 - 4x + 1 = 0$
$a = 4$ $b = -4$ $c = 1$
$$\begin{aligned} b^2 - 4ac &= (-4)^2 - 4(4)(1) \\ &= 16 - 16 \\ &= 0 \end{aligned}$$

Since the discriminant is zero, the quadratic equation has a single unique solution.

b) $6x^2 - 11x + 10 = 0$

$$a = 6 \qquad b = -11 \qquad c = 10$$
$$b^2 - 4ac = (-11)^2 - 4(6)(10)$$
$$= 121 - 240$$
$$= -119$$

Since the discriminant is negative, the quadratic equation has no real solution.

c) $8x^2 - 6x + 1 = 0$

$$a = 8 \qquad b = -6 \qquad c = 1$$
$$b^2 - 4ac = (-6)^2 - 4(8)(1)$$
$$= 36 - 32$$
$$= 4$$

Since the discriminant is positive, the quadratic equation has two distinct solutions.

Exercise Set 10.3

Determine whether each equation has two distinct solutions, a single unique solution, or no real solution.

1) $x^2 - 5x + 6 = 0$ 2) $x^2 + 2x - 10 = 0$

3) $x^2 = 7x + 5$ 4) $-8 = 2x^2 - 3x$

5) $4x^2 + 1 = 4x$ 6) $2x^2 + 5 = 2x$

Use the quadratic formula to solve each equation. If the equation has no real solution, so state.

7) $x^2 + 5x + 6 = 0$ 8) $3x^2 + 5x + 2 = 0$

9) $x^2 - x - 6 = 0$ 10) $8x^2 - 18x + 9 = 0$

11) $2 + 4x = 5x^2$ 12) $9x^2 + 2 = 6x$

13) $x^2 - 2x - 1 = 0$ 14) $8x^2 - 4x = 3$

15) The area of two squares is 765 square inches. The side of one square measures 3 inches more than the side of the other square. Find the lengths of the sides of the two squares.

16) One leg of a triangle measures 1 inch more than the other leg. If the hypotenuse is 5 inches, find the length of both legs.

Answers for Exercise Set 10.3

1) Two solutions	2) Two solutions
3) Two solutions	4) No solution
5) One solution	6) No solution
7) -3 , -2	8) -1 , - $^2/_3$
9) -2 , 3	10) $^3/_4$, $^3/_2$
11) $^{(2 -\sqrt{14})}/_5$, $^{(2 +\sqrt{14})}/_5$	12) No solution
13) 1 - $\sqrt{2}$, 1 + $\sqrt{2}$	14) $^{(1 -\sqrt{7})}/_4$, $^{(1+\sqrt{7})}/_4$,
15) 18, 21	16) 3, 4

Section 10.4 Graphing Quadratic Equations

Summary:

The graph of a quadratic equation in two variables,

$$y = ax^2 + bx + c, a \neq 0$$ is called a parabola.

To graph a quadratic equation assign convenient values to one of the variables (x) and solve the resulting equations for the corresponding values of the other variable. Plot the ordered pairs and draw a curve connecting the points.

$y = ax^2 + bx + c$ when a > 0 (positive number)
the parabola will open upward

$y = ax^2 + bx + c$ when a < 0 (negative number)
the parabola will open downward.

vertex

vertex

The **vertex** is the lowest point on a parabola that opens upward and the highest point on a graph that opens downward.

Axis of Symmetry is a line that divided the parabola into two equal halves.

Example 1. Graph $y = -x^2$

Solution: Since $a = -1$ which is less than zero, the graph will open downward.

$$y = -x^2$$

Let $x = -3$ $\quad y = -(-3)^2 = -(9)$
Let $x = -2$ $\quad y = -(-2)^2 = -(4)$
Let $x = -1$ $\quad y = -(-1)^2 = -(1)$
Let $x = 0$ $\quad y = (0)^2 = 0$
Let $x = 1$ $\quad y = -(1)^2 = -1$
Let $x = 2$ $\quad y = -(2)^2 = -4$
Let $x = 3$ $\quad y = -(3)^2 = 9$

x	y	
-3	-9	(-3, -9)
-2	-4	(-2, -4)
-1	-1	(-1, -1)
0	0	(0, 0)
1	-1	(1, -1)
2	-4	(2, -4)
3	-9	(3. -9)

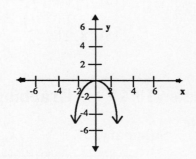

Example 2. Graph the equation $y = x^2 + 6x + 9$

Solution: Since $a = 1$ which is greater than 0, the parabola opens upward.

$$y = x^2 + 6x + 9$$

Let $x = -5$ $\quad y = (-5)^2 + 6(-5) + 9 = 4$
Let $x = -4$ $\quad y = (-4)^2 + 6(-4) + 9 = 1$
Let $x = -3$ $\quad y = (-3)^2 + 6(-3) + 9 = 0$
Let $x = -2$ $\quad y = (-2)^2 + 6(-2) + 9 = 1$
Let $x = -1$ $\quad y = (-1)^2 + 6(-1) + 9 = 4$

x	y	
-5	4	(-5, 4)
-4	1	(-4, 1)
-3	0	(-3, 0)
-2	1	(-2, 1)
-1	4	(-1, 4)

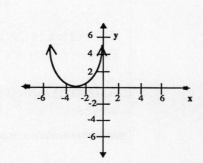

Summary:

x-coordinate of vertex	y-coordinate of vertex
(Equation of the axis of symmetry)	

$$x = {}^{-b}/_{2a} \qquad\qquad y = {}^{(4ac - b^2)}/_{4a}$$

One method to use in selecting points to plot when graphing parabolas is to determine the axis of symmetry or the vertex of the graph. Then select nearby values of **x** on either side of the axis of symmetry.

Example 3. a) Find the axis of symmetry of the equation $y = -x^2 + 4x - 3$.

b) Find the vertex of the graph.

c) Graph the equation.

Solution: **a)** $y = -x^2 + 4x - 3$ $a = -1, \; b = 4, \; c = -3$

$$x = {}^{-b}/_{2a} = {}^{-(4)}/_{2(-1)} = {}^{-4}/_{-2} = 2$$

The parabola is symmetric about the line $x = 2$.

b) The vertex is the ordered pair (2, ?).
To find y use $y = {}^{(4ac - b^2)}/_{4a}$

$$y = {}^{(4ac - b^2)}/_{4a}$$

$$y = {}^{[4(-1)(-3) - (4)^2]}/_{4(-1)}$$

$$y = {}^{12 - 16}/_{-4} \qquad y = {}^{-4}/_{-4} = 1$$

The vertex is (2, 1).

c) Since $a = -1$ which is less than zero, the graph will open downward.
$$y = -x^2 + 4x - 3$$

Let $x = 0$ $y = -(0)^2 + 4(0) - 3 = -3$
Let $x = 1$ $y = -(1)^2 + 4(1) - 3 = 0$
Let $x = 2$ $y = -(2)^2 + 4(2) - 3 = 1$
Let $x = 3$ $y = -(3)^2 + 4(3) - 3 = 0$
Let $x = 4$ $y = -(4)^2 + 4(4) - 3 = -3$

x	y	
0	-3	(0, -3)
1	0	(1, 0)
2	1	(2, 1)
3	0	(3, 0)
4	-3	(4, -3)

Summary:

The value or values of **x** where the graph crosses the **x axis** (the x intercepts) are called roots of the equation. Such points must have a **y** value to zero.

A quadratic equation of the form $y = ax^2 + bx + c$ will have either two distinct real roots, a double root, or no real roots.

Example 4. Find the roots of the equation $y = x^2 + x - 6$ graphically.

Solution: $y = x^2 + x - 6$ $\quad a = 1,$ $\quad\quad b = 1,$ $\quad\quad c = -6$

Find the axis of symmetry

$$x = {}^{-b}/_{2a} = {}^{[-(-1)]}/_{[2(1)]} = {}^{-1}/_2$$

Find the vertex of the graph whose x value is $-^1/_2$, $-^1/_2$?

$$y = {}^{(4ac - b^2)}/_{4a}$$
$$y = {}^{[4(1)(-6) - (1)^2]}/_{4(1)} = {}^{(-24 - 1)}/_4 = -\,{}^{25}/_4 \quad \text{The vertex is } -^1/_2 \, , \, {}^{-25}/_4$$

Pick values for x and find corresponding values for y.

$$y = x^2 + x - 6$$

Let x = -4 $\quad y = (-4)^2 + (-4) - 6 = 6$
Let x = -3 $\quad y = (-3)^2 + (-3) - 6 = 0$
Let x = -2 $\quad y = (-2)^2 + (-2) - 6 = -4$
Let x = -1 $\quad y = (-1)^2 + (-1) - 6 = -6$
Let x = 0 $\quad y = (0)^2 + (0) - 6 = -6$
Let x = 1 $\quad y = (1)^2 + (1) - 6 = -4$
Let x = 2 $\quad y = (2)^2 + (2) - 6 = 0$
Let x = 3 $\quad y = (3)^2 + (3) - 6 = 6$

x	y	
-4	6	(-4, 6)
-3	0	(-3, 0)
-2	-4	(-2, -4)
-1	-6	(-1, -6)
$-^1/_2$	$-^{25}/_4$	$(-^1/_2, -^{25}/_4)$
0	-6	(0, -6)
1	-4	(1, -4)
2	0	(2, 0)
3	6	(3, 6)

The roots of the equation are -3 and 2.

Exercise Set 10.4

Indicate the axis of symmetry, the coordinates of the vertex, and whether the parabola opens up or down.

1) $y = x^2 - 6x + 5$ 2) $y = x^2 + 8x + 7$

3) $y = 3x^2 - 6x$ 4) $y = x^2 - 16$

5) $y = x^2 - 2x + 3$ 6) $y = 2x^2 + 5x + 2$

Graph each quadratic equation, and determine the roots, if they exist.

7) $y = x^2 - 6x + 5$ 8) $y = x^2 + 8x + 7$

9) $y = 3x^2 - 6$ 10) $y = x^2 - 16$

11) $y = -x^2 - 2x + 3$ 12) $y = x^2 - 2x + 1$

Answers for Exercise Set 10.4

1) $x = 3$, (3, -4), up   2) $x = -4$, (-4, -9), up

3) $x = 1$, (1, -3), up   4) $x = 0$, (0, -16), up

5) $x = -1$, (-1, 4), down   6) $x = -^5/_4$, $-^{10}/_8$, $-^9/_8$, up

7)

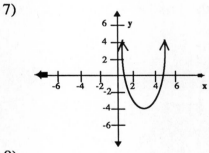

8)

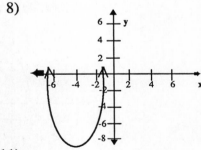

9)

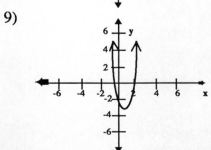

11)

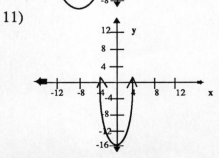

11)   12)

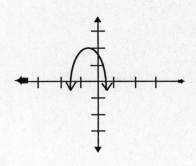   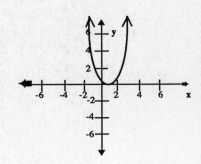

Practice Test Chapter 10

1) Solve the equation $x^2 - 7 = 0$
2) Solve the equation $(x + 5)^2 = 9$
3) Solve by completing the square: $x^2 + 1 = 6x$
4) Solve by quadratic formula: $8x^2 - 4x = 3$
5) Solve by the method of your choice: $x^2 + 7x = 84 + 2x$
6) Determine whether the following equation has two distinct real solutions, a single unique solution, or no real solutions: $x^2 - 4x + 13 = 0$
7) Indicate the axis of symmetry, the coordinates of the vertex, and whether the graph opens upward or downward:
    $y = -x^2 + 2x + 3$
8) Graph the equation $y = -x^2 + 2x + 3$ and determine the roots, if they exist.

Answers for Practice Test Chapter 10

1) $-\sqrt{7}$, $\sqrt{7}$ 2) -2, -8

3) $3 + 2\sqrt{2}$, $3 - \sqrt{2}$ 4) $(1 + \sqrt{7})/4$, $(1 - \sqrt{7})/4$

5) -12, 7   6) No real solution

7) $x = 1$, $(1, 4)$, downward

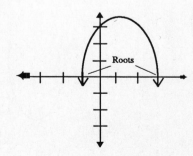

Roots are -1, 3.

❖❖❖❖❖❖❖❖❖❖❖❖❖